SCIENTISTS WHO CHANGED THE WORLD

OTHER BOOKS BY LYNN POOLE

Science Via Television
Today's Science and You
Your Trip into Space
Science the Super Sleuth
Diving for Science
Frontiers of Science
Ballooning in the Space Age

"MAKERS OF OUR MODERN WORLD" BOOKS

MODERN AMERICAN CAREER WOMEN
by Eleanor Clymer and Lillian Erlich
WOMEN OF MODERN SCIENCE
by Edna Yost
SCIENTISTS WHO CHANGED THE WORLD
by Lynn and Gray Poole

Scientists
Who Changed the World

By *LYNN* and *GRAY POOLE*

Illustrated

1960

DODD, MEAD & COMPANY · NEW YORK

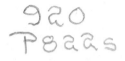
This is for
Martha, Frederick, Robert and
Richard Scholz

PREFACE

WHOM would you name if you were asked to prepare a list of scientists whose *ideas* were so new, so powerful, so revolutionary that they actually changed the world?

Your list of answers can be checked in this book against those of more than one hundred scientists and scholars who were asked the same question. The only candidates for the list were those whose thinking was creative and original.

These were not to be confused with the many great men and women who have taken the ideas of numerous scientists and synthesized them, with outstanding results. Such people have often proposed new direction for human advancement after correlating and clarifying the work of others. The contributions of that kind of scientist are valuable and frequently far-reaching but it is not the sort of person whose name you will find in this book.

The daring scientists you will read about were courageous people who devised new and revolutionary ideas that provided an entirely new way of looking at the world; whose ideas burst on the world with the force of an erupting volcano in direct opposition to already established beliefs.

The scientists in these pages affected the total structure of scientific and human development. There are other justly honored figures who made significant discoveries and developed brilliant ideas that profoundly changed the direction of thought in one specific scientific field. But those few scientists who tower above all others, who stand out as influential in changing the world, influenced concepts and techniques and changes in many scientific fields.

You will not find here the names of famous inventors. Though their inventions may seem to have changed the world, they were made possible by basic scientific facts discovered by others.

"Whom would *you* name?" brought us answers from highly respected thinkers of today who sent along pages of facts to substantiate their personal reasons for selecting scientists who changed the world. The names on all lists were checked against each other, the results tallied to find out how many of our advisers had picked the same scientists. There was unanimous agreement on the scientists we have included from Hippocrates, the ancient Greek physician, straight through to Einstein, the twentieth-century theoretical physicist.

You may not approve some of the choices. Undoubtedly you will wish that we had included other names. Nevertheless you probably agree that our destiny has been and still is directed by a few men and women of genius. The ideas and vision of enterprising and imaginative thinkers have stimulated the minds of a multitude of understanding men whose creativity in turn results in the individual discoveries and leadership that ultimately affect our lives.

Thinkers who dare to have ideas that are different are seldom popular. They arrive at conclusions that completely disrupt the safe and simple ideas in which men have believed for centuries. Disagreement with established principles and thinking often results in condemnation, public scorn, and occasionally imprisonment. It takes courage and audacity to stick to an unpopular idea in spite of ridicule and persecution.

It is our good fortune that ideas won against bigotry, and triumphed over conservative points of view. The scientific ideas you will read about here finally were accepted, and each produced such an impact, such a revolution of thought that the world was changed, that man never again looked at the world in which he lived in the same way.

CONTENTS

CONTENTS

ILLUSTRATIONS

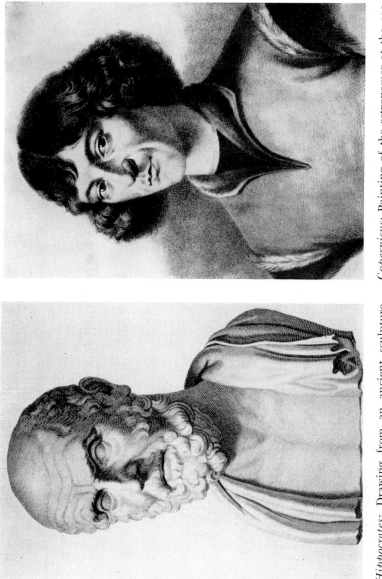

Hippocrates: Drawing from an ancient sculpture showing the father of modern medicine in old age.

Copernicus: Painting of the astronomer at the age of nineteen when he left home to study at Cracow.

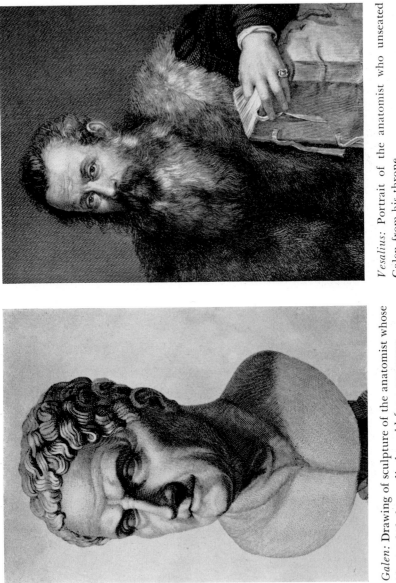

Galen: Drawing of sculpture of the anatomist whose ideas ruled the medical world for 1,300 years.

Vesalius: Portrait of the anatomist who unseated Galen from his throne.

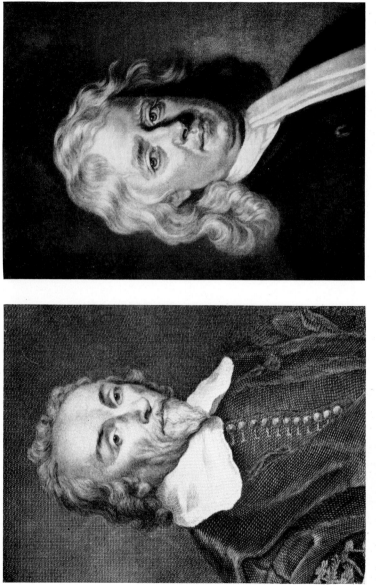

Harvey: Romanticized portrait of the man who first developed a true theory of the circulation of blood.

Newton: Arrogant genius, as he impatiently sat for his portrait during the height of his fame.

Darwin: From a portrait taken during his declining years, after the storm over his ideas had abated.

Lavoisier: Drawing of the youthful chemist made while he was working in his Paris laboratory.

Lister: A photograph of the British doctor after he had been raised to the peerage.

Pasteur: As he looked when the whole world finally honored him for his discoveries.

Marie Curie: The sad-eyed Polish woman after she had lost her husband Pierre; had discovered radium; and shared in her first Nobel Prize.

Rutherford: Sketch of the British scientist who found the key that unlocked secrets of the atom.

Freud: Cartoon sketch of the German neurologist who founded the modern science of psychoanalysis.

Einstein: German-American scientist in middle age, when he was sought after as a speaker and scientific consultant.

SCIENTISTS WHO CHANGED THE WORLD

Youthful Greek physician who dared to challenge
pagan beliefs and to establish the basic principles
of modern medicine.

HIPPOCRATES, c. 460-378 B.C.

GIANTS of science produce ideas and discoveries that burst on the world with the force and
fire of erupting volcanoes. Today we can best understand the historic contributions of such scientists by
considering the civilizations in which they lived, by
learning something of their own personal characteristics, by perceiving how their daring work changed
the way other men looked at the world.

Certain patterns develop clearly when we look at
scientists whose ideas were revolutionary. The history
of science shows that progress was stimulated by young
people who thought for themselves and had the audacity to question accepted theories and concepts.
Developments were advanced in spite of superstitions,
erroneous beliefs, or unimaginative clinging to out-
moded principles. Without delving into complex details of the scientific methods of giants of science, we

can evaluate the work that changed their own worlds, and made possible our better world.

A youth who lived in ancient Greece was typical of the giants of science of all ages. He was born at a time when a beautiful body was the ideal, when people sick with disease, fevers, and malformations were treated with abracadabra. By perseverance and at personal risk, he established sound medical practices.

Men and boys of ancient Greece took pride in their powerful physiques, physical fitness and athletic prowess. Most Greek males went daily to an outdoor gymnasium where they stripped and oiled their bodies before going out to the playing field, the track and the ring.

Greek athletes were lean and long-sinewed, never muscle-bound bruisers. Their bodies were trained to be beautiful as well as controlled. In sports contests, the athlete's performance was judged equally for graceful execution and achievement record.

The Greeks suffered from typical ailments of the athlete: sore muscles and Charley horse. They sometimes tore ligaments and broke bones in the rough and tumble of boxing and wrestling, during jumping or foot racing, or while throwing the javelin, hurling discus or weights. Injuries were treated by skilled trainers who knew from experience what to do to speed recovery. Athletic trainers were highly respected as professionals and well paid for their services.

It seems incredible that in the same country where active bodies were so perfectly trained and conditioned, sick people received very inferior treatment. The Greek man or woman who became ill sent for a priest-physician from one of the temples. The priests had little knowledge of disease so they practiced a primitive kind of mumbo jumbo. Some patients recovered in spite of the lack of proper care. Ignorant treatment caused the untimely death of many patients, others unnecessarily became chronic invalids.

Priest and patient accepted without question that illness itself was caused by some offense to one of the many Greek gods. The god had cast an evil spell on the offender who became sick. Everyone believed that an evil spell was the cause of disease and that cure could be effected only by making a sacrifice to the angry god. Sometimes food and flowers were placed on the altar of the god. Frequently a pig or a sheep was sacrificed in a temple. Often the priest would examine the insides of the slaughtered beast and would find in the gory entrails an omen, good or bad, for the sick person.

After the sacrifice had been made the priest-physician would mix herbs for the patient to take. He gave other treatments: placed charms on the body of a sick person; rattled amulets over the sickbed; or intoned incantations designed to placate the angry god. A few priest-doctors even consulted the stars to try to find out the will of the god.

The repeated rites were primitive but priest-physicians did learn from experience that certain herbs and drugs helped patients. All secrets of care and cure were jealously guarded, however, because the temple-doctors wanted to hold on to the profitable business of treating the sick. With such tight control in the hands of a very few men, it is hardly surprising that progress was slow in the priestly practice of medicine.

Revolt against soothsayers and temple-doctors started in a modest way on the Greek island of Cos off the coast of Asia Minor in the fifth century, B.C. The successful change in medical thinking and patient care which showed the way right to the doors of our twentieth-century medical schools and hospitals was led by a man called Hippocrates.

A native of Cos, Hippocrates went to train as a priest-physician at his island's Temple of Aesculapius, the mythological god supposed to have been the world's first doctor. The priest-physicians of the Temple accepted Hippocrates for training in the rituals of healing people made sick by angry gods.

In a very short time, Hippocrates discovered that

other young men in training shared his dissatisfaction with existing methods for curing patients. The group met in secret and Hippocrates, its leader, said that he was sure that illness came from earthly causes. The trainees, working on the ideas of Hippocrates, proceeded cautiously because the established temple-doctors were too powerful to defy openly in the beginning.

Hippocrates and his friends quietly treated patients who came to the Temple of Aesculapius. Under the new leadership a theory of medical practice evolved and gained favor on Cos. By the time the ruling class of temple-doctors realized what the young physicians were doing, the fame of Hippocrates and his colleagues had spread. Medical progress could not be stopped completely but the soothsaying physicians bitterly resisted it.

The methods that Hippocrates put into practice 2,300 years ago were the first to separate medicine from superstition, the first to give a scientific approach to medicine. Today every doctor takes the solemn Oath of Hippocrates dedicating his life to healing the sick by a sworn statement prepared in the fifth century B.C.

Hippocrates based his work and teaching on the firm beliefs that disease was caused by "some earthly force entering the body," or by a "breakdown of the internal organs of the body." He was convinced, too, that a doctor had to find out what caused illness before a patient could be treated.

His theories and ideas seem today to be so obvious and naïve that the simple statement of them may make us smile. But in his day the ideas were astounding and subversive. Older physicians warned that the gods would certainly punish both the disbelievers and their patients. But the group of young medical pioneers continued to work successfully with an ever-increasing number of patients.

Gradually a new school of medical thought was established and expanded. Hippocrates developed and taught methods of patient-study and care that must have seemed strange to people who previously had been treated with chanting and strange potions. In the new system the doctor found out as much as possible about the physical state of the patient when he was well. Conditions of skin, eyes and even finger-nails were checked. The doctor felt the patient's heartbeat and with ear to patient's chest listened to internal sounds.

The physical examination included questions similar to those asked by doctors today. The patient was asked about his symptoms, his feelings at the beginning of the illness and as it progressed. He was questioned about his normal diet of food and drink and about what he had eaten, what liquid he had swallowed just before he was taken sick.

In short, Hippocrates instructed his followers to take complete histories on patients, and to note down every fact as they progressed toward the *diagnosis* of illness.

Records were supposed to include facts about the house and geographical area where the patient lived so that it might be determined whether or not environment contributed to the disease. The doctor inquired about the family of the patient, checking to find out whether any relative had ever suffered from the same disease or one like it.

Hippocrates taught that it was important to find out about the character and physical stamina of a patient. He stated in terms that seem as modern as today, "Illness is sometimes stronger when a mind is troubled." He understood what we call psychosomatic medicine and realized that a troubled mind might bring on physical illness and could retard recovery.

All patients were to be gently examined and quietly questioned so that the doctor could calm their fears and gain their confidence. The writings of the Hippocratic physicians show that they were aware that a doctor could most effectively cure those patients who had faith in him.

Doctors in the fifth century B.C. knew nothing about germs, virus and bacteria. They had no wonder drugs, no thermometers, no anesthesia, and little surgical skill. It was difficult to cure most diseases and ailments but the conscientious doctors never gave up. They made the first attempts at developing *experimental medicine* by following diagnosis with treatments of various kinds. They tried "with ease" to apply poultices and to administer herbal medicines, conducting every prescribed experiment slowly and carefully, always observing the effect of treatment on a patient.

Detailed patient-records served as the first scientific "textbooks" which could be read by other physicians who wanted more information about some particular human ailment. As information about diseases and effective treatment of them increased, doctors were able to predict in general what course a specific disease would follow. They could give a *prognosis*, which is a Greek word meaning "to know beforehand."

By knowing in advance what to expect from a disease, doctors were able to tell a convalescent how to take care of himself. They could say what things he should guard against to prevent recurrence. Hippocrates urged that all doctors should keep careful check on patients even after they apparently were cured. It was necessary to learn whether aftereffects would develop, whether a patient would be susceptible to some other disease of a similar type.

Patient-care led the Hippocratic doctors directly toward *dietetics*. As they studied the sick they noted that people with certain diseases were not able to assimilate all foods. They found that some kinds of foods were best for babies, that children and young adults could eat a general, balanced diet but that aged people should eat soft foods.

Interest in diets developed into careful studies of diseases which seemed to occur in people of different age groups. Hippocratic doctors wrote "babies hiccup and cry with belly pains"; "apoplexy strikes most often between the ages of forty and sixty." It was noted that some illnesses were confined to people of advanced age and special studies were made in *geriatrics,* the study of old age and its diseases with which modern doctors are much concerned.

Epidemics were first recorded by the dedicated Greek doctors who were alert to all medical problems. When suddenly many people in one area became ill with the same disease, the scientific doctors gathered every bit of information about the possible cause of the disease and the aftereffects. Mass illness of lots of people in one local area was called *epidemos* by the doctors who were coining a new word from two: the first, *epi,* meaning around or together; and the second, *demos,* meaning a group of people. Details of an *epidemos* were written up for use by other doctors in other parts of Greece.

The first real physicians left many volumes of clinical studies and medical reports which are called the Hippocratic Writings. These cover such subjects as ulcers, surgery, fractures, fevers, mental disturbances, rare diseases and epidemics. Some of the observations, suggested treatments, prognosis, and general advice were incorrect. But modern doctors who read the Hippocratic Writings are astounded at how close to truths the ancient physicians frequently were.

The specific facts about particular conditions are inconsequential in a long-term consideration of the works. The importance of the original ideas of Hippocrates is that they changed the course of humanity by establishing a new approach to medicine. For the first time a routine of logical progression was outlined: the physician was expected to gain the confidence of a patient who was thoroughly examined before diagnosis was made. Diagnosis was to be followed with treatment, often experimental of necessity, then a complete record of every detail of the disease was set down and prognosis given. The procedure took medicine out of the realm of pagan superstition and placed it in position as a science.

Hippocrates himself traveled all over the ancient Mediterranean world teaching and lecturing, holding clinics and spreading his doctrine of belief that disease came from an earthly human source, not from the anger of the gods. He created new ideas while serving as leader of doctors who separated medicine from myth, who created a scientific approach to the study and practice of medicine.

The basic foundations and principles of modern medicine were created by a man born into an age of ignorance and superstition, a man who had ideas that changed the world.

Polish-born astronomer who waited a lifetime before publishing his conviction that the sun, not our earth, is the center of our "universe."

NICOLAUS COPERNICUS, 1473-1543

NICOLAUS COPERNICUS was born and grew up at a time when astrology influenced everyday thinking. Doctors studied astrology so that the stars could guide them in diagnosis and care of patients; political and religious leaders set dates for conferences and public events after reading the stars. Everybody consulted astrologers who by star-study predicted the future, foretold of omens good or evil.

In 1492 Nicolaus was nineteen and ready for university studies. Like any college-bound student in any time in history, he packed up his clothes and gathered together his prized possessions. Like all mothers, his gave him maternal advice, but she also insisted that he consult an astrologer before setting out on the trip from his native Torun to Cracow, site of Poland's famous university.

The Widow Corpernicus was not an ignorant

woman. She came from a well-to-do family that was respected and honored throughout Poland. Her dependence on the guidance of astrology was shared in those days by most people, educated and illiterate alike.

Her son went to the town's astrologer the night before he left for Cracow simply to please his mother. He didn't want to get into a farewell argument with her but he personally had little faith in predictions made from the stars. He was a bright teen-ager with an inquiring mind and he already had thought a great deal about the stars and their importance as guides to sailors, as the means for setting up calendars.

On the morning of Nicolaus' departure he stood in front of his family's large house with his mother. She lightly touched his hand and confidently said, "The day is right." He made no answer but only smiled. He knew she was referring to the astrologer's assurance that the journey to Cracow would be safe. It was typical of Copernicus that while he silently disagreed with the long-established beliefs in astrology, he would not openly oppose them.

Strangely enough he was headed for a life of stargazing and daydreaming that would change man's concept of the stars, planets, and what we today call our solar system. But no astrologer foresaw that future as the young man of Torun mounted a sleek, well-curried horse and rode away.

Outside the town, the powerfully built Nicolaus reined his horse and turned for a last look at his birthplace. A sad expression crossed his handsome face. He was leaving home permanently. Finally he dug his heels into his horse's flank, wheeled and rode again. His pulse quickened as he galloped toward Cracow. He was going out into the world of knowledge. No soothsayer could have told him how exciting that world was to be for him.

He took a degree in medicine, another in law, and became a canon in the Church. But as he studied first at the University of Cracow and later at the University of Bologna in Italy, he became increasingly interested in astronomy, the science concerned with the study of celestial bodies, as opposed to astrology, the commonly accepted guide for establishing horoscopes and calendars.

Until the late fifteenth century people generally believed that the world was flat. Columbus exploded that theory in 1492. The time was right for other discoveries, for free thinking, for adventures of physical exploration and of mental investigation.

Scholars for centuries had studied the planets, stars, meteors and other celestial bodies, making observations that fitted what was already accepted as fact.

People believed that their stationary earth was the center of the universe about which all planets moved. It seemed to everybody who thought at all that man was the greatest, most powerful thing in the universe —therefore, he must be the center of it.

After all, hadn't two great scholars of the past, Aristotle and Ptolemy, said the earth was the center of everything?

Three hundred years before the birth of Christ, Aristotle, the Greek scholar, stated with absolute authority that the universe was earth-centered because man was the supreme human patterned in form after the gods. Through the ages his word was accepted.

About five hundred years after Aristotle made his pronouncements, they were read by Claudius Ptolemy, an Egyptian astronomer, who, combining the theories of Aristotle with those of later astronomers and his own studies, established a doctrine concerning the universe as it was then conceived. Man and his earth remained the center of this universe. His ideas and explanations of the movement of celestial bodies were accepted by astronomers, educated laymen and the Church.

Ptolemy's power over the minds of men was so great, that his book the *Almagest,* meaning "The Greatest," remained for centuries the one astronomi-

cal guide. The *Almagest* was an encyclopedia of astronomical knowledge, containing mathematical for-
mulas, a catalogue of 1,002 stars, an explanation of the
motion of all planets revolving around the earth.
Ptolemy's beliefs were made up of a *scheme of things,*
without the physical principles to prove or disprove
the relations between planetary orbits of the many
bodies. Many of his explanations came close to fact,
but he clung to what was thought of as the universe,
with the earth in the center.

Refuting any fact stated by Ptolemy in his huge
work was as reckless and brash as ordering the sun
to stand still. But young Copernicus did challenge
some of the ideas listed as law in the *Almagest.*

From the window of his small, cold stone room at
the University of Cracow, Copernicus observed the
path of the sun and the moon as they swiftly rose and
set each day. He thought about the motion of other
planets. The longer he looked and thought, the more
he doubted that the existing laws of astronomy were
absolute and unchangeable.

For example, Ptolemy had said that Mars rode
majestically across the sky from east to west, slowed
down, stopped, and then reversed its course and
traveled back toward the east. Without proof and
without adequate instruments for verification, Copernicus came to the conclusion that this Ptolemaic

observation was an illusion. Later, in the seventeenth century, Copernicus was proved to be right, that Mars in reality moves in one direction as it revolves around the sun.

At twenty-three Copernicus went to the University of Bologna where he stayed for ten years. In Italy he was one of a small group of painters, sculptors, architects and scholars who urged each other to question old ideas, to explore new frontiers, to use their imaginations for dreaming of new concepts, new theories. He began to wonder whether the earth truly was in an immovable, fixed position. Once again he was in opposition to the information in the *Almagest*. Ptolemy had said the earth did not turn because, if it did, it would spin around and fly to pieces. Copernicus wondered why then the planets didn't fly to pieces since Ptolemy had claimed that the planets did turn on their own axes.

After much logical thought he was more firmly convinced than ever that the earth did rotate on its axis. This was one of his greatest ideas.

To him the scheme of things as devised by Ptolemy was terribly complicated. He continued to ponder the complexities of the celestial system and by logical deduction, over a long period of time, Copernicus made the boldest step of all. He removed the earth from the center of the system and replaced it with the sun. He stated that with the sun as the center of our system, with the earth and planets revolving about it, Ptolemy's complicated scheme of things became simple and logical. This was his second major contribution; one so great that it changed our world.

Conservative scholars who resented any change of ideas snapped at Copernicus. He was warned to stop this heresy, to stop being foolish and to cease questioning what was known fact. Fortunately for us, Copernicus kept thinking. Mathematics, logic and philosophy aided his expanding and daring ideas. Characteristically Copernicus avoided argument with scholars who opposed progress. He was no fiery pioneer but a scholar intent on thinking through problems posed by his own curiosity.

His major interest was the study of the universe, but he mastered the classics and made outstanding contributions to letters in the translation of Greek and Latin writing. He studied medicine, took part in the political life of his country, and worked on a practical monetary system for Poland. While he was studying in Italy, an influential uncle had obtained for him an appointment as a canon with a lifetime income.

The last thirty years of Copernicus' life were spent at Frauenburg, a little cathedral town, not far from the Baltic coast. There high on a hill in a brick tower room, he continued his astronomical investigations. It was not easy. Mist, rising from the little fresh-water lagoon on which Frauenburg was located, often prevented him from seeing the sky, the stars, the planets. Rainfall, storm clouds, and the haze typical of a moist climate made it impossible for him to keep a consistent record of the movements of astral bodies. The telescope had not yet been invented.

Patiently he continued his thinking, always making careful notes, keeping records as complete as possible. He talked with his friends about his beliefs and theories, and about a book he was writing. His conversations were reported to other scholars and soon murmurs of disapproval were heard. Some claimed that the ideas of Copernicus were heretical and he should be burned at the stake. Martin Luther and other religious leaders protested the changes in the system of the universe and called Copernicus fool as well as heretic.

Copernicus was in a delicate position. The Catholic and Protestant churches accepted the earth as the center of the sixteenth-century universe. And, when the Church believed something, that was that. To go against the teachings of the Church was to flirt with probable excommunication, invite certain persecution and risk possible burning at the stake. Copernicus had the daring to think for himself but he lacked the courage to stand up and fight for his ideas.

Once again Copernicus backed away from conflict. He stated often that he would prefer never to publish his book rather than to have it create a war of ideas. But doggedly as ever he continued to work on his project in private.

For thirty-six years, he worked on his *De revolutionibus orbium coelestium* which was to change the world. The book described how he had decided on a system which took the earth from the center of the universe and replaced it with the sun. He explained how simple the theory was and how beautiful, to him. With the sun occupying the center of the universe, all else fell neatly into a logical pattern. According to his system, the stars, planets, and all objects in the firmament now followed an orderly path around the sun.

The finished manuscript contained Copernicus' concise conclusions which placed the sun in the center of the solar system, as well as his more sketchy mathematical and astronomical calculations. The work was written by hand in flawless Latin, and the titles and initial words were handsomely scripted in red ink. The completed work was a precise statement of original thought by a man of imagination and vision.

When Copernicus was sixty-six years old he was

visited by a young German mathematician who called himself Rheticus. The twenty-five-year-old scholar from Wittenberg expected to stay at Frauenburg for only two weeks but he remained for two years, always urging Copernicus to publish his book, to share his revolutionary ideas with scholars of the world.

The time in which Copernicus lived was confusing and distressing for scholars. Universities were filled with men who had original ideas, who evolved new concepts of history, geography, mathematics and other subjects. But most leaders, political and religious, were opposed to ideas and concepts which changed or refuted accepted facts. Copernicus knew perfectly well that many scholars had been killed for contradicting ideas from the past. He would not back down from what he believed but he had not the forcefulness deliberately to stir up trouble. His nature, retiring and peaceable, was that of a serious and sincere scholar. He knew that his thinking was right but he lacked both the courage and the desire to fight for his beliefs.

The reluctance of Copernicus to crusade for his ideas and the reasons for that hesitance were understood by Rheticus. But he had the foresight to see that the Copernican theory of the universe had to be widely distributed. He realized that the world must know about the new ideas. Finally he forced the issue.

Rheticus himself published a pamphlet entitled *First Account* in which he brilliantly stated the discoveries of Copernicus and specifically set down the beliefs of Copernicus. The pamphlet was distributed to learned men throughout Europe. As Copernicus had feared, violent protests came from those conventional scholars and narrow-minded leaders who were resistant to new ideas. Religious leaders threatened him with excommunication.

Although Copernicus did not reprimand Rheticus for his audacity in writing *First Account,* he was more adamant than ever against publication of his own life work.

Rheticus and other friends of Copernicus were determined that Copernicus should see his book, his great contribution to the world, before he died. Time was running out. Copernicus was old, and had had a stroke.

The manuscript was sent to Nuremberg for printing with all possible speed. The printer took one look at the radical words and turned pale. At first he refused to print the book. But his objections were waved away by the strong-minded, determined Rheticus.

In late May, 1543, the first copy of *De revolutionibus* was rushed to Frauenburg where Copernicus lay dying. The volume was placed in its author's hands. Copernicus stared at the book, looked up at the friends standing by his bedside, but said nothing. No one knows whether he knew what he was holding. Within a few hours he was dead.

The pamphlet by Rheticus had caused a furor but the book itself created no immediate reaction. Few people understood it, fewer cared about it one way or another. Some shrugged it off by saying, "Ptolemy still remains supreme." It was not until Giordano Bruno, an Italian philosopher and scientist, began to spread the Copernican concept across the whole of Europe that the trouble began. The astronomical system was branded as heretical, godless, and fanatical by teachers in the classroom and by clerics in the pulpit. Undaunted, Bruno continued to teach the new theory of the solar system until 1600 when he was condemned to death and burned at the stake, a martyr for the cause of Copernicus.

More scholars died because of their belief in the idea of a solar-centered system which today seems to us to be so obvious. Scholars testing the theory decided that Copernicus had been correct in many of his conclusions. Galileo Galilei, the great Italian astronomer, early accepted the Copernican theory and for fifteen years taught it to his students. Finally the Church condemned Galileo who, at the age of seventy, escaped Bruno's fate by renouncing what he knew to be true. "Ptolemy was the correct scholar," falsely nodded the aged Galileo who knew better. His was a pitiful act for a scientist who in all other ways was so great.

By choosing the sun for the center of his system, Copernicus opened the door to space, started the true investigation of our solar system. He toppled man from the center of everything, made man a minute speck on the edge of infinity. So great was the change and so immense the contribution that there is no doubt that Copernicus created the first stage of the platform from which today's sun-circling rockets are launched into outer space.

Three medical scientists who dared to be different and to disprove ideas which had been blindly followed for centuries.

CLAUDIUS GALEN, c. 130-200

ANDREAS VESALIUS, 1514-1564

WILLIAM HARVEY, 1578-1657

MAN'S scientific study of his own anatomy dates back for many centuries to a Greek who dissected Barbary apes; to a Belgian who stole cadavers for autopsy; to an Englishman who experimented with rabbits. These men were physicians to rulers and royalty but their places in medical history are not dependent on the prominence of their patients. Each of the three doctors revolutionized medical thinking in his own time and added vital knowledge about our bodies.

Today we appreciate the human body as a marvel of design. It is at once delicate and strong. It moves with the precision of a machine but with the freedom of a floating leaf. Individual sections of the body are thread-thin, feather-light, air-filled, yet the whole has a strength that can withstand incredible degrees of heat and cold, amazing amounts of pressure and fatigue, excruciating pain from injury or disease.

The subjects of anatomy, biology and physiology, as we understand them, were nonexistent until the mid-sixteenth century. At that time men of medical science were shocked by the publication of a book on human anatomy that defied the teachings and theories of the Greek physician, Galen. His statements about the human body had been unquestioned for more than 1,300 years. In the early seventeenth century scientists were roused by a book on the circulation of the blood which refuted the claims of Galen on that subject.

The two publications, which appeared within one century (1543 and 1628), were written by men who disproved many of Galen's deductions but gave him great credit for his pioneering work in anatomy.

Galen, like Hippocrates, was a Greek from Asia Minor. He was born in the early part of the second century, A.D., and was the son of wealthy parents. He was an intelligent youngster but showed no childhood interest in science. It was expected that he would have a career in commerce until the night his father had a dream which directly changed the course of Galen's life, and indirectly the course of medical history.

The father, who believed in dream-prophecy, awoke one morning and announced that he had dreamed that Galen was a physician. At once the youth was sent to begin his medical studies in the ancient city of Pergamum. Galen was still in Pergamum when his father died leaving him a large inheritance. The fortune gave Galen the funds and freedom to travel widely in search of more knowledge of medicine, a subject which he fortunately had found absorbing.

Finally he arrived in Italy where he soon established a reputation as a respected doctor to the rulers and merchants of Rome. Another man might have been content simply to practice medicine, to lead a fairly leisurely life of ease. But Galen had become a dedicated scientist with the inquiring mind of a true scholar. He was determined to extend medical knowledge beyond the narrow limits within which it was then practiced. He read widely in the literature of medical procedures and experimentation. His special interest was anatomy.

Galen was impatient to find answers to hundreds of anatomical questions beginning with such elementary ones as: What are the parts of the body? How do they function? What are the tissues and muscles that cover the skeleton of bones? He wanted to find answers scientifically through research and experimentation but he could not—and would not—learn from dead bodies of human beings.

The Romans believed that the human body was a godlike figure which could not be defiled in any way. Galen shared that philosophical and religious attitude so he was forced at first to make his anatomical deductions from observation. He had to find out what he could from examining the outside of the body, from feeling the bone structure, the muscle formations and movements. The general acceptance of the Roman body as a thing of divine origin prevented the practice of autopsy and dissection.

It was the body of the Roman citizen, incidentally, that was supposed to be sacred, and not the human body of slaves, and people from other countries, of other races. Romans swarmed to public amphitheaters to see humans torn apart by wild beasts. Citizens of Rome, who cheered and shouted from the tiers surrounding the arena, were delighted by savage exhibitions in which captives, disobedient slaves, and Christian martyrs were dismembered and devoured by lions.

The very thought of those bloody spectacles appalls us. We find it difficult to reconcile Roman enjoyment of brutality to the living with the opposition of Romans to post-mortem dissection.

Galen's dissections were limited to Barbary apes, a tailless species. He believed that the bodily functions of ape and man were identical and wrote many volumes about physiology and anatomy based on that mistaken premise.

Month after month he dissected apes. He used his knife with skill and kept detailed notes on his examinations. Galen's writings contain information about the organs, muscles and blood within the body; about the functions of the ape liver, heart, spinal cord and brain. He stated that blood formed in the liver and flowed through the body until it reached the heart. There, according to Galen's theory, the blood mixed with divine spirits and passed on to the brain where it was infused with animal spirits and then flowed to the ends of the nerves to stimulate the motion-functions of the body.

Much of Galen's research and teaching was done after he became personal physician to Marcus Aurelius, philosopher and Roman Emperor. If Galen had continued in the general practice of medicine, he wouldn't have had time for his own studies, nor for his students.

He was a stern but inspiring teacher and insisted that his medical students dissect the bodies of apes. He didn't want the young scientists to accept what he said as fact but to see for themselves that what he wrote was true. He believed that they should learn from experience.

With single-minded purpose, Galen played an important role in the development of medicine. He was one of medicine's great teachers, investigators and writers. He added immeasurably to the understanding of anatomy. Of course, he made mistakes. Some of his observations and many of his interpretations were incorrect. Nonetheless his total contribution was vital to medical progress.

Galen's reputation was so outstanding, his conclusions were presented so logically, that his findings were accepted as absolute facts for 1,300 years. Century after century medical men taught anatomy and physiology to students who used the writings of Galen as gospel and textbook. From time to time some student or physician would dare to point out a discrepancy between what he saw and what Galen wrote. Galen himself would have encouraged these men to think for themselves, but their teachers and colleagues scornfully said, "You are wrong. Look again. Galen made no errors."

A successful, major challenge to Galen's teachings was delayed until the sixteenth century. It came from Andreas Vesalius who caused a revolution in medical thought comparable to the revolution in astronomical thinking started by Copernicus in the same century.

Andreas, son of a Brussels physician, was born in Belgium in 1514. He was a sturdy, handsome little boy who was bright and smart in school. Although he developed strong muscles and was bursting with physical energy, he didn't go in for athletics. He actually scoffed at his schoolmates who wasted their time competing in sports. A jealous nature made him resentful if any other pupil made a better grade than he. He was scornful of youngsters who spent all their free time playing. His idea of fun was to read medical books and scientific treatises.

From early childhood he was fascinated by the form and structure of living things. His curiosity about insects and animals led him to dissection with instruments that he had sneaked out of his father's surgical cabinets. This father didn't need to dream that his son would be a doctor. It was quite evident that Andreas would follow his father's profession. When the elder Vesalius fully realized the extent of Andreas' interest in science, he encouraged him. Together they built a small laboratory where Andreas could experiment. He once said in jest that he was going to slash his own muscles to find out how they were put together, how they moved. The joke amused his father but his mother trembled for fear her son really would mutilate himself.

One winter's night, Andreas called his father into the little lab. On a counter was a dissected cat and next to it a copy of a work by Galen. Andreas pointed out to his father that facts in the book did not agree with what he had seen in the cat carcass. That incident established the pattern of Andreas' professional life.

Whenever he discovered a variance between the written word and his own laboratory experiments, he followed the subject to a tested conclusion. After proving a fact to his own satisfaction he stated it vehemently, often tactlessly. He arrogantly challenged any medical or other scientific opinion with which he did not agree.

The young Vesalius entered the University of Louvain as an honor graduate from school. From Louvain, he went to Paris to study medicine. There he was extremely unpopular with professors and with fellow-students who referred to him as *"that* Vesalius!" He made no effort to get along with other students. Because of his early reading and precocious experimenting, he was much more advanced than they, and he made it clear that he felt superior to them.

In anatomy classes, Vesalius was restless and impatient with the professors whom he annoyed. The method of instruction followed one set pattern: a professor, enthroned in a sort of bishop's chair, read from the works of Galen. Below the professor's platform, an assistant dissected an animal, exposing the particular part of the body referred to in the passage from Galen.

Years later Vesalius writing about these classes to his patron, Charles V of Spain, remembered that the professors all droned on "never departing from him [Galen] by so much as the breadth of a nail." He recalled too that no doctor admitted "that even the slightest error has been found."

Vesalius' professors were painfully aware that the young medical student was not in agreement with them or with Galen. Sometimes he would get up noisily and stalk out of the lecture hall muttering to himself. Often he boldly spoke up to point out a conflict between what the professor was reading and what was being seen in the dissected animal. More than once he made the shocking proposal that human anatomy should be learned from human bodies.

No one thought that Vesalius could possibly be serious. It was well known that there was a French law against the dissection of human bodies. Risk of arrest and imprisonment could not stop Vesalius. He decided on a bold and dangerous plan. He himself would find dead bodies of human beings and would dissect them in secret.

Fearlessly he roamed at night through the country looking for a corpse. One night he discovered the body of a dead man hanging from a tree. He cut the rope, hoisted the limp figure up onto his strong, wide shoulders and walked to his room.

There, with the writings of Galen before him, Vesalius read about the dissections of the Barbary apes. Then, using special instruments he himself had designed, he meticulously dissected the human body. Following Galen's scientific pattern, he made careful notes on the dissecting methods, on his observations. In addition, he recorded the differences between ape and man.

Vesalius' second corpse was that of an executed criminal whose body had been thrown on a dump. The body was so decomposed that only ligaments and the skeleton were left. Vesalius again wrote down his precise notes and also made anatomical drawings.

When Vesalius was only twenty-three years old he was asked to conduct anatomical studies at the University of Padua, in Italy. Once more he was at odds with other medical men and was egotistically indifferent to their opinions. With the assistance of an ever-increasing number of younger students, he continued his dissections and physiological experiments.

While at Padua, Vesalius began a book on anatomy, *De humani corporis fabrica* (The Working of the Human Body), which was published in 1543. The book's preface contained both a tribute to Galen and a criticism of those who had followed Galen's writings without question, without verifying facts for themselves. In the text, Vesalius noted and illustrated the differences between his conclusions and Galen's. Throughout the book, however, Vesalius conscientiously reminded his readers that his dissections were made on human bodies, Galen's on Barbary apes.

In spite of Vesalius' scholarly and explicit scientific presentation, his book created a storm of protest. He was violently criticized for daring to question the writings of Galen, for attacking medical scientists who slavishly accepted Galen's word as "gospel, unchangeable and sanctified."

Vesalius was infuriated by the reaction to his book. He knew that he had pioneered a new approach to the study of anatomy, that his work would lead to rapid developments in medical research. How rapid, he didn't realize. Very soon scientists published medical papers that were illustrated with drawings based on experiments originally made by Vesalius. Instead of being pleased by evidence of the acknowledged value of his work, Vesalius was angry. He went into jealous rages and accused colleagues of stealing his ideas. In a huff, he left Padua and crossed the sea to Spain. There, as court physician, he was doctor first to Charles V and later to his son, Philip II.

Within the limitations of his time, Vesalius had produced a work that influenced studies not only of anatomy and physiology but of biology and other related fields. He gave the world a new understanding of anatomy that was vital to medical progress.

Anatomical studies had been static for 1,300 years when Vesalius began his research. After he had opened the way, scientific knowledge of the human body advanced steadily. Just eighty-five years after Vesalius' book was published, William Harvey crossed another frontier of medical research.

Harvey was born in England on April 1, 1578. Like Galen and Vesalius, he was the son of rich parents. He, too, grew up with advantages provided by a prosperous family.

Medicine fascinated him from the time he was a small boy. At an early age he read the works of Aristotle, Hippocrates, Galen and Vesalius. When he was still young, he dissected domestic animals, rabbits and guinea pigs, and commented on the conflicting findings of Vesalius and Galen. He gave his youthful opinion that Vesalius was correct in his evaluation of Galen's errors. But Harvey questioned some of Vesalius' original work which he was able to study in the light of discoveries made after Vesalius' book was published.

Harvey finished his courses at Cambridge University and went to the University of Padua where Vesalius had done his important research and writing. At that Italian university Harvey found Galileo who was teaching and adding to the concepts so brilliantly stated by Copernicus in the fifteenth century. Many other outstanding men of ideas were doing research in science at Padua. Harvey continued his own studies in anatomy and general medicine.

His curiosity centered on the movement of blood through the body. He was not held back, as Galen had been, by metaphysical and philosophical theories. Harvey was free to plunge enthusiastically into the study of the blood stream.

The young Englishman was an expert dissecter and he patiently conducted numerous experiments at Padua before returning to Cambridge to take his medical degree. With the patronage of the famous Dr. Lancelot Browne, physician to Her Majesty Queen Elizabeth I, Harvey established a medical practice. This provided him with enough free time to continue his research work. When Elizabeth died, Harvey became physician to King James I. From the king he received permission to dissect specimens of the finest animals from the Royal Park.

The result of Harvey's investigations is accepted today by all medical men as one of the greatest ad-

vances in medical history. He established the fact
that blood *circulates* in the body and that it does not
flow from liver to heart to brain in the circuitous
route guessed at by Galen. It was Harvey who charted
the exact course of the blood as it circulates through
the human body.

We know that blood circulates, so that statement
seems commonplace to us. But in 1628 when Harvey
published his *Exercitatio anatomica de motu cordis
et sanguinis in animalibus* (Dissertation Concerning
the Motion of the Heart and Blood in Animals) the
work created an explosion. The publication brought
Harvey to the attention of the entire scientific world,
not only of medical circles.

Harvey's careful study of the action of the heart,
the arteries and the veins made order out of what had
been a chaotic system, simplified what had seemed
complex. Within the careful notes of his investigations, we find his proven theory that the heart is divided into a left auricle and left ventricle, a right
ventricle, a right auricle. The body's blood, about six
quarts, is pumped from the left ventricle to circulate
through the arteries, veins and capillaries. Some of
the blood goes through the liver and kidneys and
circulates to every part of the body before returning
to the right auricle, down into the right ventricle
from which the blood passes to the lungs to receive

oxygen before passing into the left auricle and down into the left ventricle where it begins its circulation all over again.

Simply stated this is the major path the blood follows as it circulates throughout the body. It is difficult for us to understand that the explanation was not accepted by everyone in Harvey's day. However, his system was in direct opposition to long-established teachings and beliefs, so some medical scientists repudiated his theory. Other scientists couldn't see what difference it made how the blood got through the body anyway.

Harvey haughtily ignored his detractors. So far as he was concerned, he agreed with those who hailed his contribution as important. He didn't care whether lesser people accepted it or not. He had explained a physiological phenomenon with scientific proof and for him that was an achievement of which he was proud. Actually his work revolutionized the science of medicine, probably to a greater degree than even he realized.

Galen—Vesalius—Harvey. These three men laid the foundations for the understanding of man, a marvel of design. Others have built on their foundations, and that construction continues today as we grow ever closer to complete understanding of the human body.

Young British physicist whose astounding theories upset the scientific world and pointed the way to the future.

ISAAC NEWTON, 1642-1727

ASK ten people the question "Who discovered gravity?" and you are likely to get nine answers: "Isaac Newton. He was sleeping in an orchard when an apple dropped on his head and he had a bright idea about falling objects."

The accepted anecdote about Newton and the apple is half-myth, half-truth. His contributions to the advancement of science did include many laws of gravity, and his original thinking on the subject was sparked by an apple. However, scientists had known of the existence of gravitation long before Isaac Newton was born on Christmas Day, 1642.

As a small boy, Isaac was an enthusiastic model-builder. Unlike the hobby-models of most youngsters, his were exceptional. They were ingeniously conceived, meticulously made with perfection of working parts, of minute details. By the time he was a teen-ager he was constructing windmills, water clocks, sundials and kites with lantern attachments that he flew at night.

He was a very poor student in the classroom but very good at the projects which interested him. He took no part in children's games and made no school friends. He preferred to stay by himself working with models and reading and keeping private notebooks.

When Newton was sixteen, he left school to help his mother run the family farm at Woolsthorpe in Lincolnshire, England. At farming he was completely undependable. Neglecting his chores, he hid in quiet corners of house and barn reading books and making drawings and scribbling calculations. He had a passion for asking difficult questions and since no one could answer them to his satisfaction, he set out to find the answers himself.

In desperation, his mother sent him back to school where he could be prepared for Trinity College, Cambridge, which he entered in 1661 when he was eighteen years old. At Trinity the familiar pattern was repeated. He didn't do well in his studies and he stayed to himself, avoiding the social activities of the university. His manner was arrogant and egotistical, and he was equally unpopular with professors and students.

Newton was discouraged and about to leave the

university when he met Dr. Isaac Barrow, an eminent mathematician, philosopher and Greek scholar. Dr. Barrow recognized Newton's capabilities and became his tutor. Almost overnight Newton changed from a lackadaisical student into an eager scholar who studied joyfully.

He delved into what was then the most complicated mathematics; read everything he could find on the subject of light; pored over Copernican theories and the writings of Galileo; plunged headlong through the complex works of Johannes Kepler; and puzzled over the science of optics.

The writings of famous men of knowledge spurred Newton to a real fury of investigation. He challenged ideas of scholars of the past, insisted on finding proof of stated facts. Again he posed questions that no one else could answer.

Formulation of the *right questions* was the basis of Newton's genius and probably was his greatest contribution to scientific method. Newton himself wrote, "Asking the correct question is half the problem. Once the question is formulated there remains to be found only proof [an answer] of that question. The path to the proof is then direct."

That seemed a simple statement to Newton but to his colleagues it made little sense. They were not accustomed to using the questioning approach to cut through the complexities they found and observed while doing research. Newton realized that scientists could and did endlessly gather facts and amass observations without productive results. He believed that progress was possible only when a scientist asked himself what the facts and observations meant. The one right question, according to Newton, would unravel the secrets from a mass of information and could pinpoint an answer of scientific value.

A trick of fate gave him the time he needed to think through the questions that gripped him. A bubonic plague, which swept over England, closed Cambridge in 1665. Newton returned to the farm at Woolsthorpe and during the time that the university was closed began the creative thinking which produced answers for him and for all scientists.

Newton unwittingly started the legend of the apple. He wrote that while at home because of the plague quarantine, he was sitting in his garden when he saw an apple fall to the ground. According to his own notes, that action made him reconsider gravity.

He previously had pondered about all kinds of mechanical motion, the movement of the planets, and gravitation. The movement of planets had been described by Copernicus, Galileo and Kepler, but these scientists had given no definite mathematical and mechanical proof of, or reasons for, the orbits.

The great astronomers had plotted the motion of the planets and the movements of things on earth but they had given no answer to WHY? or HOW? the planets were held in exact orbits.

The falling apple led Newton to his *inverse square law of gravitation*. That law states that any two bodies in the universe attract each other with a force directly proportional to the product of their masses and inversely proportional to the square of the distance between them.

To a man with a mind like Newton's, believing was not certainty. He had to prove his theory and there was available no mathematics precise enough to work out his proof. Laboriously and brilliantly, Newton invented an entire new system of mathematics—calculus. He devised *integral* and *differential calculus* over a period of years, then applied this "most amazing and unearthly feat of mathematical creation" to proving how and why celestial bodies move as they do.

Although Newton devised the new mathematics for a specific reason, he unknowingly gave to the scientific world an entirely new approach to physical, chemical and biological problems. Much of today's scientific research is dependent on calculus. As a new science it immediately broadened the horizons of scientific investigation.

When Newton completed his studies of celestial motion to his own satisfaction, his restless, inquiring mind turned to the subject of light and optics. Light had been a subject of interest to scientists for centuries, and Newton was no exception. While on his enforced and welcomed holiday from Cambridge, he studied the properties of light, first reviewing in his mind what already was known about it.

In ancient Greece, it was believed that every object emitted small particles that bombarded the eye to create an image of the object. Later, Plato supposed that vision was produced by a triple interaction of the rays of the sun, the object viewed, and the human eye. Theories and experiments with light and optics continued through the centuries. Eyeglasses and telescopes were developed in the Middle Ages.

In Newton's century, the seventeenth, Francesco Maria Grimaldi, Italian physicist and Jesuit priest, discovered and named the phenomenon of *diffraction,* the breaking up of light when it is reflected from lined surfaces or is passed through a fine slit or a prism. England's Robert Hooke, a contemporary of Newton, held the theory that light was a sort of wave. But no one yet knew the content of white light.

Newton began to experiment with white light, working as he always did with precision and care. First he confirmed Grimaldi's discovery by cutting, in heavy paper, a tiny hole through which sunlight could flow. On the side opposite the source of sunlight, he placed a prism. The sunlight went through the prism and cast a rectangular image. The image was five times as long as it was wide and showed all the colors of the spectrum. Light, then, was not a single ray but many rays of many colors. Over and over again, Newton experimented with the light and the hole. Each time the image was rectangular with the colors falling into the same pattern and position.

It was obvious that each color in white light was bent or *refracted* in the same way every time it passed through the prism. The questioning Newton wanted to know what made red bend the least, violet the most.

He ran test after test in an attempt to separate the colors. Finally he set up a prism through which he beamed light at a small hole in a board. On the other side of the board he set up a second prism. Now he found that the light could be controlled. He manipulated the first prism so that only one color at a time went through the hole and he could refract each color individually. By this method he established the fact that each color has a different degree of refraction.

Newton's curiosity carried him beyond the prism test. Having found that rays of different colors refract at different angles, he wondered what happened when light struck a mirror. Careful experiments with light reflected from a mirror gave results that amazed even Newton. All rays of all colors reflect from a mirror at the same angle. This fact gave Newton an idea.

Telescopes up to that time had been made with two lenses and as a result images were distorted. Newton believed that one lens and one mirror would provide a better image. He had been an expert model-maker since early childhood and now he constructed a model telescope. He substituted for the second lens a mirror which he had polished to a high brightness. The combination of one lens with one mirror worked. Newton gave to the world of science the first modern telescope, a type which has been improved through the years. Nevertheless, the largest reflecting telescope in the world, the 200-inch observatory telescope on Mt. Palomar in California, and others of all sizes are constructed on the basic principle of Newton's first small experimental model.

Newton's experiments with light caused a sensation among the members of England's Royal Society, an organization of which he was a Fellow. He had made major scientific contributions: the discovery that color was a basic property of white light; and the development of the reflecting telescope. His work with the spectra of light has become a fundamental keystone of modern physics enabling scientists to analyze the chemical compositions of all organic substances. The reflecting telescope has made it possible for man to probe deeply into the physical properties of our world, and to look out into space.

Praise and honors were lavished on Newton who brushed off friends, colleagues and scientist-admirers. He neglected to answer letters begging him to lecture on his new discoveries, but engaged in acid correspondence with scientists and others with whom he had some imagined grievance. Newton was a genius with a strange personality, who in two years, when he was twenty-two and twenty-three years old, did the basic work upon which his fame is justified. His scientific achievements were limitless and of immeasurable value and he should have been content with his freedom to work and research, and with his attainments. Instead he was eager for power and money, and petty in most human relationships.

At least once Newton threatened to resign from the Royal Society and he often was uncooperative about making his findings available to members. Only after persistent urging did he finally give one of his telescopes to the Society where it is now preserved as one of the world's great scientific treasures.

Newton's contributions to physical science include three laws of motion. His first law states: An object in motion moves at a constant speed in a straight line unless influenced by a force. A simplified illustration of the law is an express wagon pushed along a sidewalk. It continues to roll until the opposing force of friction gradually slows it down.

His second law says: An outside force acting on an object moves the object in the direction of the force. Again the wagon given a push rolls in the direction of the applied force.

Newton's third law states: For every action there is an equal and opposite reaction. If a boy standing at the rear of the express wagon jumps off the wagon, the wagon will go in the opposite direction to the jump.

For all the years that Newton taught and studied at Cambridge, he poured out ideas. He created principles of proven facts by the hundreds. These were written on torn scraps of paper, scribbled in notebooks, or recorded only in his head. He gave no thought to publishing any of his findings. Unlike Copernicus who was afraid that publication might bring ridicule and persecution, Newton was simply not interested in gathering together his information. Once he had proved a theory or established a law for his own purposes of experimentation and research, he was no longer concerned with the facts and details.

He first used calculus without recording it on paper and only set down the mathematical notations when another scientists wanted to use the process for computation.

It was Edmund Halley, the British astronomer, who finally persuaded Newton that he should prepare his vast mass of scientific information for publication. Newton began in 1684 and within fifteen months had assembled all the material and notes and had written in Latin a first draft of his *Philosophiae naturalis principia mathematica* or "Mathematical Principles of Natural Philosophy."

Perfecting and completing the project was too much for the impatient Newton. He asked a friend to recommend to him a young man capable of being a research assistant who also could copy the completed manuscript for the printer. As a result of that request Isaac Newton's manuscript copy of *Principia,* another treasure housed at London's Royal Society, is handwritten in neat Latin by Humphrey Newton, who was not related to the great scientist whose masterpiece he copied for the printer.

Isaac Newton lived to be an old man and became increasingly irritable and opionated with the passing years. After he left the academic life at Cambridge, he dabbled in politics and was appointed Director of the Mint. He attained the wealth for which he had always been greedy and in the end lived in the luxury he had yearned for in his youth. His complex personality made him a controversial figure in the world of science, but not even his own unfortunate nature could detract from the scientific fame he so justly deserved.

His contribution to the world was more than calculus, optics, mechanics and gravity. He led physical science out of the Middle Ages and pointed the way to the future. Some will say that as twentieth-century science has developed Newton's facts have been disproved and replaced. We should be aware of this attitude but should beware of its implication. True, science has changed and gone beyond Newtonian physics, *but the shift has been an extension* of his ideas, a growth of new areas of physics made possible by his work on which modern science is based.

Newton's amazing concepts were like a rock, dropped into a pond, that creates a ripple. The force of the rock and ripple creates other ripples in an ever-widening circle. The concepts (rock) that Newton tossed into the scientific world (the pond) still remain strong and basic.

In a real sense we live in an age predicted and made possible by Isaac Newton, a strange, erratic and vain man who changed the world with the freedom, daring and brilliance of his thinking.

French chemist, elected to the Academy of Sciences at the early age of twenty-five, whose creative experimentation is the basis for modern chemistry.

ANTOINE LAURENT LAVOISIER, 1743-1794

FRANCE during the eighteenth century was a country of contradictions. The aristocracy lived in fabulous luxury; the lower classes in miserable poverty. Courtiers presented spectacular pageants in ballroom and garden; mobs rioted with violence in village and town. Under the rule of the Bourbon kings, Louis XIV, Louis XV, and Louis XVI, the turbulent nation was aflame with reform, abounding in new ideas.

One of the famous men of that age of discord and progress was Antoine Laurent Lavoisier whose name now is familiar to comparatively few people. He was a man of vision who instituted social reform, worked diligently in economics, and ingeniously founded modern chemistry.

Lavoisier was born in Paris on May 8, 1743. He received a degree in law which he had studied only because it was the wish of his father, a successful lawyer. Young Lavoisier never practiced, however. He took his degree and went straight to his scientific laboratory where he began research in many areas of science. His early success in geology and chemistry was so outstanding that he was elected to the French Academy of Sciences in 1768 when he was only twenty-five.

Although his family had money and he was certain of a large inheritance, Lavoisier wanted to be personally independent. On the advice of friends he invested money in the *ferme générale,* an organization which collected taxes for the king. In effect he became a tax collector and his percentage from the company gave him the independence he wanted so that he might continue his scientific research.

Lavoisier's body was slight and wiry but his limitless energy gave him strength to function in many different areas of interest. He owned a 1,200-acre farm which he personally operated at a good profit. The way he managed the farm and kept accurate statistics of crop production indicated that he had a mind, keen and analytical, that was typical of the research scientist.

He conceived the idea that the grain from each section of his farm had a direct relation to the amount of manure dropped on that section. With precision he calculated how many head of cattle should be allowed to roam each field. By increasing the size of herds and rotating crops, he was able to double the grain yield within a very few years. His experiment antedated scientific farming by a century.

Lavoisier's interest in farming led him naturally to active membership in the Agriculture Society of Paris and ultimately to an appointment to the Agriculture Commission. Imagine the stir caused by the aristocratic gentleman from Paris when he toured rural France. Farmers whose land he inspected must have been astounded by the sight of the commissioner who wore elegantly tailored clothes, cuffed in lace and fluffed at the neckline with billowing jabot.

His combined abilities in science and business made him invaluable as a consultant. Among other things, he was adviser to the government on the production and distribution of gunpowder. With reckless disregard for his own personal safety, the dynamic aristocrat took part in dangerous experiments with explosives. Once he came within inches of losing his life in a blast that did kill two other experimenters.

Lavoisier was liberal in his thinking and so dedicated to social reform that he frequently disagreed on policy with the king and his ministers. When the monarchy was overthrown and forced to accept a popular constitution and National Assembly, Lavoi-

sier was made head of the financial institution which
eventually became the Bank of France. He instituted
tax reforms, urged new agricultural methods, and
outlined a basic economic system for the Republic
after the execution of Louis XVI.

His plans for general public education were based
on a daring concept. He believed that every child in
France should be provided with an education through
the elementary and secondary school ages. In a country where illiteracy was widespread that idea was
sensational. His influence in the field of education
spread across the Atlantic Ocean to Virginia where
his ideas guided the men who established a college
in Richmond.

Lavoisier had a brilliant mind and was an indefatigable worker, but even so he couldn't have carried
on his serious scientific research without help. His
invaluable assistant was his amazing wife, Marie
Anne Pierrette Paulze Lavoisier. They were married
in 1771 when he was twenty-eight and his bride not
quite fourteen. From the beginning Marie Lavoisier's imagination was fired by her husband's exciting dreams of the future of science.

The teen-age girl, dedicated to contributing to her
husband's research activities, learned English and
Latin so she could translate scientific papers and
books for him. As Lavoisier became more involved

in his numerous projects, his wife condensed articles and even books so he could quickly be informed on scientific subjects. When he began his own scientific writings, she made drawings and even engraved plates for illustrations of his books and pamphlets.

The Lavoisiers entertained elaborately in their Paris home where Madame Lavoisier was a gracious hostess who dressed with exquisite taste. Certainly few of the guests, who included scientists, economists, statesmen and landowner-farmers, were aware that Madame Lavoisier, devoted wife and woman of charm, also was a science expert.

The science of chemistry was stagnant when Lavoisier began his research. Most chemists conducted experiments based on what they believed to be established principles, and discarded developments which failed to fit into the supposedly well-founded patterns of chemistry.

In the hundred years preceding Lavoisier's experimentations, one of the most important of the accepted principles was the *phlogiston theory*. That was a highly complex theory which basically was concerned with combustion. Chemists thought that when a material burned it released what they called phlogiston, the substance which actually made the material combustible.

Lavoisier was one of the first scientists to understand the fundamental nature of combustion by recognizing chemical changes; one of the first to prove basic facts about chemical combustion.

Spurred by the riddles of combustion he began a series of experiments on the oxidation of tin. When he burned tin he found that the ash weighed more than the tin had weighed before it had been burned. Understandably he was puzzled. How could the ashes weigh *more* if the substance called phlogiston was released by the burning? Shouldn't the ash weigh less if part of the material really went up in smoke and was given off into the air by the burning?

Continuing with his research he turned to phosphorus. Using the most delicate instruments and balances available to him, he weighed the phosphorus and then burned it. Again, the ash weighed more than the original amount of phosphorus.

His final answer came from another experiment. He captured gases escaping from the burning of sulphur. When he weighed the gases he found they also weighed more than the original sample of sulphur. This led him to believe that a material when burned *does not throw off* a substance but absorbs air; that, for example, during the combustion process, oxygen from the air is incorporated with sulphur to produce gases. Naturally if the gases are incorporated with air they would weigh more.

Lavoisier picked up the clue to proof of his theory from Joseph Priestley, an outstanding British scientist, who produced what he called "dephlogisticated air," air without phlogiston in it. Lavoisier called the dephlogisticated air *oxygen* and set about to prove that when combustion takes place a material does absorb oxygen.

With proven data and by irrefutable experiments, Lavoisier upset the existing theory of phlogiston. He replaced that theory with the correct one that combustion and oxidation resulted from the chemical combination of the material with oxygen.

Some scientific experts hailed the Lavoisier theory, but Lavoisier had no time to take bows for his work. He was busy attending meetings of bankers, speaking to farm groups, and conferring with chemists. His attention turned to a problem that was a natural outgrowth of combustion research but was concerned with human beings and animals, not with inanimate matter in test tubes. Body heat and energy were the subjects of studies which stimulated Lavoisier to extensive research.

It was an accepted fact that human and animal life depended on something taken into the lungs and body from the air. The questions that intrigued Lavoisier were: What was that something? How did it act?

Again the clue was provided by the distinguished Dr. Priestley who found that breath exhaled by animals was heavy with carbon dioxide. As soon as Lavoisier learned of Priestley's discovery, he gathered a laboratory staff and began experimentation with animals. Lavoisier already knew that sugars and fats in the body can be broken down when they combine with oxygen, and be made to give off carbon dioxide. With test-animals, he proved that heat was produced in the body when oxygen combines with carbon compounds. The heat was a result of combustion.

Through a series of meticulous experiments, Lavoisier was able to determine the exact amount of oxygen taken into the body, to calculate the combustion within the body, to measure the heat and carbon dioxide given off. These experiments led to the development of the new science of calorimetry—the science of the measurement of heat. Calorimetry is vital to chemical, biochemical, medical, physiological, biological and nuclear research.

Lavoisier extended his studies to include the actual measurement of the heat produced and energy consumed at various rates of body activity. The experiments proved that increased exercise, by man or beast, resulted in greater oxygen intake, produced more heat and energy. Lavoisier noted, too, that during periods of increased exercise his laboratory animals ate more food. Although he did not follow the food consumption experiments to finished conclusions, many scientists today say that with them he introduced the science of nutrition.

The history of science indicates that progress is achieved when order replaces confusion, when complexity is reduced to simplicity. One of Lavoisier's great contributions to the advancement of science was made through a simplification of terminology. It irked him that the nomenclature for chemical substances, elements, compounds and techniques followed no orderly pattern. Names almost never had any relationship to the thing or process to which they were given.

Lavoisier and his co-workers drew up a table of elements, a table of terminology, which still exists and, with only minor variations, is used by twentieth-century chemists. The lists have been extended as new elements have been discovered but the terminology still is based on Lavoisier's system.

The "shorthand" of chemistry is another of Lavoisier's contributions. He thought that chemists should have a simple means for expressing themselves in writing and speech. It was his idea that cumbersome, lengthy and wordy descriptions should be reduced so that meanings could be understood by everyone. In other words, he established verbal chemical equations. For example, instead of using two hundred words to describe a chemical reaction in fermentation, Lavoisier wrote it this way: Fermentation = alcohol + acid + oxygen.

Later, chemical equations were changed from words to symbols. The best known symbol probably is H_2O (water), though students of elementary chemistry everywhere recognize the symbols: CO_2, and C_2H_5OH.

No one claims that every detail of Lavoisier's scientific work was correct. He made errors due to limited concepts, techniques and knowledge of his time. He succeeded, however, in raising chemists from their minor position in science, by stimulating their imaginations, by interesting them in experimental research. Through his own research he disproved the phlogiston theory; redirected the field of combustion; planted the seed of organic analysis and nutritional study; set up terminology still used today; and replaced complex words and methods with simple terms and processes.

"Father of modern chemistry"; "founder of modern chemistry"; "leader of contemporary chemical approach"; "originator of modern chemical methods"—all these and many more titles have been given to Lavoisier, an energetic French scientist, whose zest for life was boundless.

Within his own lifetime he was honored for his chemical theories but he was killed by his countrymen, the very citizens of France he wanted so much to help. After King Louis XVI was guillotined in 1793 and the French Republic was set up, the people turned against Lavoisier. They forgot, almost overnight, his liberal ideas, land and tax reforms, stable monetary system, educational plans and his criticisms of the court. In the mass hysteria of the French Revolution, Lavoisier was identified with the hated monarchists. In that revolution, as in others, extremists and terrorists sought revenge and ever-increasing power. Scapegoats, as always, suffered with the guilty.

Lavoisier was arrested on trumped-up charges and imprisoned as a traitor to the people. He was dragged before the Revolutionary Tribunal on the morning of May 8, 1794, supposedly to be given a fair hearing. The trial was a swift mockery. Before sundown Lavoisier's head rolled into a basket set under a guillotine.

The following day, Joseph Lagrange, eminent French mathematician, made the remark that became the epitaph of Antoine Lavoisier: "It took only a moment to sever that head and perhaps a century may not be sufficient to produce another like it."

Sensitive and brilliant English naturalist who enjoyed ill health and disliked the revolution he started by publication of his book *Origin of Species*.

CHARLES DARWIN, 1809-1882

ONE of the most remarkable success stories in science is that of a naturalist who got off to a bad start in life. Charles Darwin was a puny child, a sickly youth, a poor student, and in his early years appeared to be a misfit in a family of robust, energetic, intellectual people.

For a long time it seemed as if Charles were one Darwin who would never succeed at anything. Even his father who was supposed to have an ability to read other people's thoughts did not foresee that his fifth child would eventually write a book which would change the way man looks at his past, present and future.

Charles was born in Shrewsbury, England, on February 12, 1809. His mother was a member of the Wedgwood family which gave its name to the long-famed English china. His father, Robert Waring

Darwin, was a wealthy physician with a tremendous physique, an overpowering personality, and a zest for life which overwhelmed everyone.

The scrawny, quiet Charles was awed by his dynamic father and by the family's older children. He bumbled along in school and failed to make the grade in medicine, the profession his doctor-father wanted him to follow. It was at Cambridge University, where he was preparing for the ministry, that Charles was encouraged by several naturalists to develop his interest in their field of study.

As a boy Charles had collected shells, rocks and fossils. At Cambridge through the efforts of a professor of botany he became seriously interested in accumulating all sorts of specimens from nature. He showed such aptitude for cataloguing and recording what he found that it was not surprising that he was recommended as a naturalist to a British expedition of exploration.

The older and outstanding naturalists who suggested him to the expedition's captain could not be away from their universities and laboratories for extended travel. But they had faith in the abilities of young Darwin, who had the time for a long voyage.

The proposed trip of exploration to strange areas of the world made Charles physically sick for two reasons: anticipation and fear. He was excited by the prospect of studying plants, mammals and birds in distant lands. It scared him to go because he was afraid of the water and knew that he was subject to seasickness. In spite of his fears he set sail with the group aboard the "H.M.S. Beagle" on December 27, 1831, for a voyage that lasted nearly five years during which he was miserably seasick a good bit of the time.

The "Beagle" sailed to Cape Verde Islands, South America, the Galapagos Islands, New Zealand, Australia, many other Pacific islands, and then home around the Cape of Good Hope. Everywhere the ship anchored, Darwin went ashore to study the plant and animal life.

In previous short trips around the British Isles, Darwin had made observations that strengthened his interest in where, when and how life began. A number of theories had been previously stated: that the world and everything on and in it had been created at one time; that life had been evolved by some dark and devious method from nonliving matter.

Conditioned by his upbringing in the Unitarian Church, noted for its encouragement of freedom of thought, Darwin had studied the existing theories and had begun to develop ideas of his own based on his studies of living and nonliving things. He believed that the answers to the questions about the beginning of life were buried in the remains of the past.

He had an inquiring mind, a curiosity about natural things, and a dedication to test and to prove scientifically what he believed. Like every true scientist he insisted that each theory be supported by fact. His drive toward this end pushed him to work in foreign lands even when he was ill, convalescent and weak.

On the voyage of the "Beagle" Charles Darwin took so many notes and made so many sketches that he returned with dozens of notebooks. His collection of countless specimens filled hundreds of boxes of several sizes. Later, in thinking back on this trip, he realized that all the time he had unconsciously been amassing proof of an orderly evolution. He scientifically studied his notes, specimens and sketches for years before he wrote *Origin of Species,* the book which was to revolutionize completely the way man approached and solved the questions: "Where did all living matter come from?" "How did it arrive in its present forms?"

Immediately after his return, Darwin lived in London while he worked on the material gathered during the voyage. Shortly afterward he married Susan Wedgwood, a cousin, and they moved to an elegant country estate in Kent. Charles and his wife were both wealthy so he could, and did, spend his life working on his concept of the logical, evolutionary development of the living world.

Through constant, patient, daily study, Darwin concluded that all existing forms of matter and life, both plant and animal, resulted from a long-involved evolution that progressed from the simple to the complex. Gradually his ideas about evolution took definite shape, followed precise patterns.

The theory of evolution holds that all life today traces itself back to the very beginning of time. How far back into what endless ages no one knows even now. Today we know that life may have started with minerals in the earth which gave birth to a primitive free-living virus gene form, a minute living speck on earth. The virus may then have developed into a primitive cell without a nucleus, then into a cell with a nucleus containing genes. Again the cell with genes divided to produce a wide variety of organisms which brought forth animals and plants.

Proceeding from the most elementary and tiniest forms of life, evolution took place with an ever-widening growth until finally man in all his complexity came into being. Evolution continues constantly.

The theory of evolution is rightly associated with Darwin's name. It must be realized, however, that a general concept of evolution is a very ancient one. Darwin's specific and great contribution was twofold. Not only was he the first person to gather an overwhelming mass of data as evidence of the reality of evolution, but he also was the first person to develop a satisfactory theory of how this evolution takes place and the mechanisms by which it occurs.

After we accept the idea of evolution to explain the millions of varieties of living things on earth, we have only just touched the subject. What remained to be done in Darwin's time, and since, was to discover clues to the mechanisms by which organisms not only could continue to reproduce their kind but also could provide the change that is responsible for the increasing variety of living things that exist.

From his study of matter, mammals, fish and plants Darwin reasoned that it was impossible for all species, all matter, all living things and their millions of varieties, to have sprung into existence at one time.

Think about the variety for a moment. We see it every day in many kinds of trees, animals, flowers, plants, birds and people. Look at plants: there are nearly a million different species of plants existing in our world today and they keep on coming. They change with changing weather which is itself evolving, changing.

Look at insects: there are a half a million different kinds of insects. Look at people: they are all human beings but the variation can be measured by the total world population. To get a personal sense of variety study your own hand. Hold it up. The tip of your finger, which can give a fingerprint, is unique. No other person in the world has the identical fingerprint. An identical twin has the same skin as the other identical in a pair, but identical twins do not have the same fingerprints, so that even identical twins are not exactly alike in all things.

Similarly, every living organism has any number of "fingerprints" of differences that make the organism uniquely different from every other member of its species.

Darwin's notebooks were crammed with facts about, and drawings of, living things of the same species. His notes and sketches showed the individual differences. Let's examine two examples from the thousands he recorded. In the valley of Tierra del Fuego he was impressed with a moderate but obvious amount of distinction among animals which suggested that modifications were local and not the result of crossbreeding with animals from other areas of the world. In the Galapagos Islands, he saw fourteen different species of small, drab-colored, finchlike birds. Some had long bills and some short; between were finches with bills of varying lengths.

He was curious about individual differences. His collections of fossils and living organisms confirmed his theory that existing animals have a close relationship with ancient, extinct species. He observed birds and their migrations which gave rise to a change within a species. Still he questioned "Why?" more especially he questioned "What?" changed any species in a defined and remote location like the Galapagos Islands.

His theory of evolution provided clues to what he called the *variation of the species*. Let's examine those clues. We know that more organisms come into existence than can obtain nourishment and survive. One oyster produces up to 114,000,000 eggs in one single spawning. Obviously all eggs cannot live and become oysters. Since we know that the number of each species remains fairly constant under normal conditions, we must assume that most of the offspring perish. If they didn't there would be disaster on earth.

One single bacterium that is 1/125,000 of an inch long, reproducing at the rate of one every half hour would create a mass larger than this earth within a month or so. One maple tree, full-grown, produces hundreds of thousands of seeds each year. Only a few seeds live to produce new maple trees. Even man, who reproduces at a relatively slow rate, is fast outgrowing his living space. Not all of any one of the many varieties of one species can possibly survive.

Since more individuals (plants, animals and humans) are born than can possibly survive, there is competition for survival, a struggle to maintain life. The idea of the *survival of the fittest* is the core of Darwin's theory of natural selection. Competition between different species, as well as between individuals within the same species, allows only the most fit to survive. Nature itself by imposing burdens on life, permits only the most fit to exist except where man himself has been able to keep the less fit alive.

The surviving species and variations within species give rise to future, stronger generations and in this way successful characteristics are transmitted to succeeding generations. Successive generations become better fitted to their environments. As the environment changes, other variations are evolved to fit the environment. And so it goes endlessly in the evolution of living things.

By studying fossils and through his own observation of living things, Darwin found that, in the fight for survival, members of one species will leave their natural environment in an attempt to remain alive. The survivors in a new environment will adapt themselves by undergoing certain physical changes. Cows and deer evolved digestive organs that would enable them to feed on foliage. Birds took to the air as efficient flying machines and then shore birds, a variety of a species, adapted themselves to areas where they could obtain food by developing feet for scuttling through grass and walking in water. Those organisms which are not adaptable to new environmental conditions do not survive. With this in mind, Darwin's concept of evolution for which he produced irrefutable evidence was this:

1. Animals reproduce in much greater numbers than can possibly be supported by the environment in which they live, and more than is necessary to maintain the species.

2. As a result great numbers of individuals within each species must be destroyed. Therefore, there must be a struggle for existence, and a *survival of the fittest, not only among the animals of a single species but also between the many different species.*

3. Animals of the same species vary in their structure, and Darwin assumed these variations of structure within the same species must be inherited. Only in this way (inheritance) can the best structures be passed on from one generation to another.

4. During the struggle of existence, *natural selection* will act so that the best animals within a species will survive. By inheriting the best characteristics, surviving individuals within a species will gradually become better adapted to their environment. This evolution within the species will in time change and give rise to a new species.

Variations occur slowly but continuously. Evolution continues every second of every day. Man, the human being, is the highest form of life which has evolved from the immeasurable past and man, with his mind, can look back to study his own progress, can look ahead to future evolution.

Darwin's theory with its scientific notations and conclusions changed the world. Like Copernicus he knew that his idea was controversial and he hesitated to make public his theory and his scientific substantiation. *Origin of Species* was published in 1859, and every copy was sold on the first day. Immediately the author was reviled and berated. Darwin went into a state of nervous collapse when he was challenged to debate by a great clerical orator, Bishop Samuel Wilberforce. Thomas Huxley, a friend and champion of Darwin's, accepted the Bishop's challenge and the debate was held in Oxford. The Bishop ridiculed Darwin; Huxley defended him brilliantly. The audience was in turmoil. Gentlemen, normally controlled and reasonable, engaged in fisticuffs; a lady of the peerage fainted.

The battle against Darwin's theory was in full swing. The offensive was taken by those who failed to see that Darwin's ideas were substantiated with scientific data, by those who resented any change. The attack against evolution did not begin to subside until after the famous 1925 Scopes trial of a young

Tennessee school teacher who had been arrested for teaching the theory of evolution. People had the misconception that evolution meant only that human beings were descended from apes. The development of men, who think and reason, from earlier forms of mammalian life is just one step in the theory and by now man has become reconciled to strange relatives of many ages past.

At the time of the Scopes trial most people knew little about Darwin's scientific theory and even less about the scientific data which he had collected and studied for many years. Some few men of serious scientific purpose had begun to use Darwin's idea as a guide in their own research. In laboratories, scientists studied plants, their genes and crossbreeding, as well as the living cells of humans and animals. Other scientists examining fossils in the earth saw there the progression of development of the ages which gave proof of evolution.

The impact of the theory on biological study was tremendous. Darwin's idea meant that discoveries made in bacterium, a mouse and a plant might be applied equally well to man. Medical scientists noted that all living things react in a similar way. Giving unity to life, the theory showed that the elephant and the lettuce leaf are akin and obey the same physical, chemical and biological laws.

The theory gave a new approach to the study of fossils which was a step forward in geology. Changes in the earth's crust, the shifting of seas, the growth of mountains, all proved to be the products of evolution.

Physics and chemistry were re-examined in the light of the theory with emphasis on the kinds of atoms and how they came into existence from more primitive structures. Understanding of our solar system and the total universe of millions of galaxies was increased and changed by the new knowledge of the mechanism of evolution.

The discovery of genes in all living matter came after Darwin but it further proved the greatness of his contribution to science. With knowledge gained through the study of genetics we now know reasonably well *how* evolution takes place, *what* evolution has produced, and *why* evolution is an integral part of the life cycle.

As we said earlier, for centuries men had been thinking in various ways about the development of life on this earth, of a kind of evolution. During Darwin's day reputable men of science were coming closer to an understanding of evolution. Alfred Russel Wallace, working completely independently, had come to much the same conclusion as had Darwin. Yet, it was Darwin's creative genius which makes him justly known as the founder of the modern theory of evolution.

No one can claim that Darwin understood the full implications of his theory. He didn't. Scientists for a century now have been carrying forward his work far beyond even his enlightened vision. But everybody gives credit to Darwin for giving voice and proof to the ideas which changed the course of thinking about how life began. He struck the spark, igniting the flame which illuminated the facts of evolution. Other men of curiosity, imagination and dedication to scientific study are keeping the flame burning.

Morton was the American doctor who first performed painless surgery. Lister was the English
surgeon who fought for antiseptic methods in hospitals.

WILLIAM T. G. MORTON, 1819-1868
JOSEPH LISTER, 1827-1912

MANY of us are alive today because one
man, a British doctor, put up a fight for cleanliness
in hospital and sickroom, waged war against germs
and infection. We have teeth extracted painlessly
and can be blissfully unconscious during tonsil and
appendix operations because a few brave doctors
dared to experiment with putting patients "to sleep."
The physician who chased dirt and those who cru-
saded for painless treatment were not dwellers in
the dark ages. They practiced medicine in the nineteenth century.

We enter a quiet, spick and span, modern hospital
without thinking about what such institutions were
like just a hundred years ago. Rooms were dirty and
unswept. Bed linen was changed not oftener than

once a week, if then. Halls rang with the screams of patients undergoing operations, and wards reverberated with the moans of those suffering from post-operative gangrene.

Doctors didn't put on white jackets for visiting hospital patients, nor did they don surgical gowns for operating. Wearing long black coats they went from house to hospital, from patient to patient, from morgue to operating room. The dust-covered and germ-specked coats were unsanitary garments that made the doctors look forbidding. The general effect of solemnity was heightened by stiffly starched shirt collars held in place with black ties.

Most people fought to keep from being hospitalized. Patients waiting at home for an operation shuddered when they heard the wheels of the surgeon's carriage, trembled when he entered the house, shook with horrible fright at the sight of his crude instruments laid out on a bedside table. Strong men, hired to hold down the patient, gripped ankles and shoulders while the patient shouted in agony through the terrible ordeal.

Relatives prayed and wept over a surgery patient at home or in the hospital. In either place operations were touch-and-go affairs. Incisions almost always became infected and pus poured from the wounds. Too often gangrene set in with fatal results.

Physicians and surgeons were sympathetic to patients and their relatives but they could offer no assurance that healing would follow an operation. Doctors simply shrugged their shoulders and, of necessity, left recovery to chance.

A little more than a century ago the words *medicine, hospital, operation, surgery,* made people turn cold with fear for themselves and for loved ones. Frequently the treatment of an illness was worse than the sickness itself. An eminent Viennese doctor, Friedrich Manholtz, wrote in 1838, "Could we only take away the stark pain of surgery and prevent the inevitable suppuration [pus, infection] we would change man's attitude toward the world in which he lives."

Four years later, one method for taking away the "stark pain of surgery" was tried in the United States. Actually the means for conducting painless surgery had been available for three hundred years. In 1540, Valerius Cordus discovered a volatile liquid, well known to us as the anesthetic, ether. If the properties which made it useful to medical science had been recognized in the sixteenth century, thousands of patients could have been relieved of the pain that Dr. Manholtz so regretted.

Joseph Priestley, in 1772, discovered *nitrous oxide,* a gas that exhilarated people who inhaled it. Michael

Faraday experimented with the physical effects of both ether and nitrous oxide in 1818. In 1824, a German doctor put experimental laboratory animals to sleep with nitrous oxide.

Doctors wished that there was some way to relieve the suffering of surgery patients. Through the ages surgery had been direct torture, and only two means had been found for giving even partial relief from pain during an operation. Both of these were drastic: the first was to knock out the patient with a powerful blow so he would be spared a few minutes of the agony of cutting. A second was to fill the patient with whiskey in the hope that he would pass into an alcoholic stupor. A third method sometimes was provided by nature when the tormented patient fainted.

An American physician, Dr. Crawford W. Long of Jefferson, Georgia, after reading about the properties of ether and nitrous oxide, searched until he found a patient willing to try gas inhalation. In March 1842, Dr. Long administered carefully controlled amounts of gas to the patient from whose neck he removed a tumor. That operation was the first ever performed on a patient under anesthesia. When the patient came to, he was overjoyed at having been spared the pain of surgery. It was Dr. Long who suffered from the experiment. He was abused by his fellow-citizens for taking a chance with the gas, and was forced to stop what they called the "in-human witchcraft."

A few years later a young dentist, Dr. William T. G. Morton, working with Dr. Horace Wells, in Massachusetts, extracted teeth using gas to put patients to sleep. Dr. Wells convinced friends at the Harvard Medical School that a surgical operation also could be performed with the patient asleep.

A demonstration was arranged for members of the medical faculty and students. The group was skeptical. When the patient was wheeled in, students nudged and winked at each other; faculty members tried not to show their disapproval. The gas was administered and the patient seemed to fall into deep sleep. Then something went wrong. With the first cut of the surgeon's knife, the patient came to, screaming. The operating room was in an uproar. Students jeered and laughed. Faculty members angrily stalked out muttering about "charlatans."

Dr. Morton was discouraged but not defeated. He registered as a student in the Harvard Medical School where he assured Dr. John Warren that the blessings of painless surgery could be obtained through the use of gas that Dr. Morton called *letheon*. Dr. Warren, chief of surgery at the Massachusetts General Hospital and professor of surgery at Harvard, somewhat reluctantly agreed to a second demonstration-operation. A neck-tumor operation was scheduled for October 16, 1846, and on the morning of that day the patient was wheeled into the operating amphitheater. Once again there was a large group of doctors and students in attendance.

Minutes passed and nothing happened. Dr. Morton had not arrived. More time went by. The professional audience grew restless and started to mumble about the "quack with the sleep-gas." When a few doctors started to leave, Dr. Warren asked that they wait for a few minutes more and, out of respect for the great surgeon, the group quieted down and waited.

Suddenly the door was flung open and a breathless Dr. Morton dashed in. Over the face of the patient he placed a cloth mask which had been especially prepared for the operation. Slowly he dropped a liquid on the mask. The patient breathed deeply and within a few minutes was asleep. The tumor was removed. The patient returned to consciousness.

This time the doctors and students left the operating room with a different kind of excitement. Corridors buzzed with discussion of the painless operation, a surgical miracle that could be repeated over and over again throughout the world.

Surgeons from other places did not rush to find out about the painless surgery. At first only those who saw the Harvard demonstration were convinced of the usefulness of the method. Newspapers and even medical journals printed scathing stories about the "quacks in Boston." But little by little the idea of operations performed on patients under gas was accepted by laymen and doctors. Oliver Wendell Holmes, New England's famous author, physician and scholar gave enthusiastic approval to the use of gas for putting surgical patients to sleep. It was he who named the process *anesthesia,* from the Greek word meaning insensibility.

Dr. Morton's contribution might well place him on a list of scientists who changed the world, even if his daring work were confined to the field of surgery. But his contribution went far beyond its use for operations. Anesthesia allowed medical men to learn more about the human body, its functions and diseases. Chemists and biochemists, physicists and biophysicists, biologists and anatomists found it to be a tool which opened new frontiers in their scientific explorations. Many more fields of scientific investigation were made possible by the anesthesia even though one first thinks of the triumph over pain during surgery and the psychological reactions to such an experience.

Man's attitude toward surgery slowly changed when he no longer had to suffer physical torment during an operation. So the first part of Dr. Friedrich Manholtz' wish had come true. But throughout the world, people by the thousands continued to die from the "inevitable suppuration," infection and gangrene, brought on by lack of hygienic conditions. Germ control was unknown and the need for cleanliness was not even recognized as a problem in hospitals.

A young British doctor, while studying surgery at the University of Edinburgh, became very much aware of the relationship of dirt to infection. Joseph Lister, son of a wealthy merchant, received his undergraduate training at University College in London and was twenty-six years old when he left for Edinburgh in 1853. The serious-minded young Quaker was horrified by the unsanitary conditions in hospitals, appalled by the high death rate caused by infection.

On his rounds of hospital wards he saw that no one used any method of *asepsis,* the prevention of infection which produced pus and gangrene. He knew that there was no method of *antisepsis,* the cure of infection after it had set in.

It distressed Lister to see doctors and students go directly from the morgue where corpses were dissected to the operating room where patients awaited surgery. The doctors and students didn't change clothes, though during a morgue autopsy they might have been in contact with some contagious germ; they didn't disinfect themselves, and only washed their hands if they thought about that precaution.

Lister talked incessantly about what might be done to prevent deaths from infection and continuously cautioned his colleagues about the need for cleanliness. He was considered to be a little queer on the subject and doctors often scooted down side halls to avoid Lister who might buttonhole them for a lecture on his favorite topic.

Many doctors actually disagreed with his ideas and clung to the ancient belief that infection was useful, that it cleaned out disease. For centuries doctors had thought that "laudable pus" was the way by which the body sloughed off disease. Lister was sure that "laudable pus" did not originate inside the body. He was certain that it formed outside, entered the body, spread through the system, and killed the patient more often than not.

After reading about Louis Pasteur's theory that microorganisms (germs) suspended in the air caused fermentation and putrefaction, Lister was more than ever convinced of his own conclusion about "laudable pus." He did not think a wound could become infected from contact with pure air. It had to be germs in the air that settled on wounds and caused a type of fermentation—infection—which very frequently resulted in gangrene.

The big questions that Lister had to answer were: How could infection be stopped once it began? How could the wound be treated to kill the germs?

When Lister read that carbolic acid was being poured into sewers to slow down or stop fermentation, he suggested to his bored colleagues that carbolic acid in weak solution might kill germs of infection. Of course, his friends laughed at him.

But Lister wasn't a man to be discouraged by ridicule. His first use of carbolic acid followed a minor operation. When his surgery was completed, he soaked a piece of cloth in a weak solution of carbolic acid and with clean forceps swabbed the incision with the liquid. He put a second piece of solution-soaked cloth over the wound and covered the bandage with a thin metal plate to slow down or prevent evaporation of the carbolic acid. Within a week the wound was healing with only a very little pus showing on the slightly infected incision area.

The same week Lister performed a more complicated operation. A thirteen-year-old boy had had his left arm caught in a machine. Part of the arm bone was sticking out of badly torn skin. Muscles in the arm were lacerated and dangling. In those days the accepted treatment for that kind of severe compound fracture was amputation in the hope of saving the patient's life.

Lister refused to amputate the arm. Instead, working swiftly, he sewed the muscles together, set the fracture, cleaned the entire bloody area with a solution of carbolic acid stronger than the first one he had used. After sewing up the skin, he wrapped the entire arm in heavy cloth soaked in the carbolic acid solution. The wet cloth was covered with layer upon layer of protective outer bandage. For days Lister saw his teen-age patient almost every hour. The boy showed no symptoms of severe infection. His temperature was normal, his appetite good. Five days after the operation, Lister hopefully removed the bandages. The arm showed only the slightest sign of infection. (The boy lived and had the use of his left arm for life.)

The success of the treatment of the arm was shrugged off as sheer luck by Lister's colleagues. The reaction of other doctors didn't disturb Lister. He was worrying about the tiny amount of infection and how even it could have been prevented.

He wasn't long discovering the cause of the infection. It was in the catgut, the surgical cord, with which he had sewn the mutilated arm. Lister always had insisted that his operating room instruments and utensils be kept clean, but he had overlooked the fact that surgical thread was not sterile. It was kept in the open air where dust and germs could settle on it.

Lister began to close all incisions with catgut and surgical needles that were dipped in the carbolic acid solution just minutes before he used them. He found that this procedure not only prevented postoperative infection but also stopped any open-wound infection that had set in before operation.

Soon he had to face another problem. Surgeons in those days lacked proper instruments with which to tie off arteries and veins, and a steady flow of blood inevitably followed certain operations even after the skin had been sewed up. When blood continued to seep from the patient, infection developed. In such cases the application of soaked cloths failed to stop infection.

Lister spent long hours in his laboratory experimenting with the problem set up by bleeding after surgery. Finally he mixed a putty antiseptic made from powdered carbonate-of-lime moistened with his antiseptic solution of carbolic acid. He spread a quarter-inch of putty over a surgical wound, then placed a soaked cloth on the putty. The cloth was covered with the metal shield and the wound area was wrapped in heavier bandage. The blood continued to seep up under the putty but there was no growth of infecton.

The death rate in the Lister ward at the hospital in Edinburgh dropped almost to zero. Still his skeptical fellow-doctors were not convinced that his methods were responsible for the impressive record of patient-recovery. "No one can stop infection once it begins," they said. "Lister is just lucky."

Lister dared other doctors to allow him to put some of his patients in their wards where deaths from infection were high. If his patients pulled through and theirs continued to die, there would be proof that his treatments were responsible for the lowered death rate. No one would accept Lister's challenge. He fought his battle alone.

While he worked on antisepsis following surgery, he got the idea that purification of air in the operating room would get rid of the germs that contributed to infection. He prepared a solution of carbolic acid that was sprayed around the operating room. This attempt was not successful. A spray powerful enough to kill germs in the air would have been too strong for inhalation by doctors, nurses and patients.

The news of Lister's achievements spread throughout Europe where surgeons in France, Germany and Italy used his antiseptic techniques with success. Surgeons from the United States traveled to watch Lister at work, to study his methods. But for a long time in his native England, he was considered to be a crackpot.

It was years after he began his unpopular crusade that Joseph Lister won full recognition in his own country. He finally was raised to the peerage by Queen Victoria and ultimately was showered with many other well-deserved honors. Oliver Wendell Holmes observed that in spite of opposition that was almost persecution, Lord Lister made historical contributions to the world of medicine.

Jenner, an Englishman, and Pasteur, a Frenchman, proved that human beings could be vaccinated and inoculated against diseases.

EDWARD JENNER, 1749-1823
LOUIS PASTEUR, 1822-1895

TWO boys were key figures in two of the major medical events of all time. History was made when healthy James Phipps, age nine, was given experimental inoculations against smallpox by Edward Jenner, an eighteenth-century doctor; when dog-bitten Joseph Meister, age nine, received preventive inoculations against rabies from Louis Pasteur, a nineteenth-century French chemist.

Dreadful diseases do not just disappear by themselves. They have to be wiped out, destroyed, controlled. Scientists have found ways to check and even exterminate many communicable diseases that once raged in epidemics.

Black Death, spread by fleas from infested rats, and yellow fever, a mosquito-carried virus, are just terms that we read in books today, thanks to science. But bubonic plague, aptly called Black Death, sweeping through Europe in the fourteenth century, reputedly killed a quarter of the population of the continent. Until the turn of the twentieth century, countless thousands of people, living in hot swamp countries, wasted away from the effects of yellow fever.

Schistosomiasis is one of today's devastating diseases but we can hope that soon it, too, will be a matter of history. Scientists are making every effort to conquer the fatal schistosomiasis, transmitted by a parasite worm from a host snail, that still is a threat to 115,-000,000 people in tropic areas throughout the world.

The efforts of scientists have reduced many once-terrifying ailments to the status of sporadic diseases. Some of those that now show up only sporadically, in either isolated geographic areas or as incidental, individual cases, are malaria, typhoid fever, and the smallpox and rabies mentioned above. Even polio is being brought under control.

Smallpox is a sporadic disease but, not so long ago, it killed thousands of people every year and left many more victims with disfiguring lifetime scars. In 1732 an epidemic of smallpox crossed Central Europe and stabbed its deathly prongs into France. French doctors, exhausted from spending sleepless nights with

ill and dying patients, expressed the futile wish that
something could be done to prevent death-dealing
epidemics of the frightful disease.

Four years later the virulent smallpox broke out
in England. There a doctor suggested to colleagues
that a record be kept of the number of patients ill
with smallpox. But he sadly agreed when they argued
that it was a waste of valuable time to keep records
when nothing could be done about the disease.

Later in the eighteenth century, a record-keeping
British doctor found at last that something could be
done about smallpox.

Edward Jenner, a physician living and practicing
in rural England, was a well-trained and inquisitive
scientist who understood the value of continuing research. Before he began his studies of smallpox, he
had been made a Fellow of the Royal Society as a
result of scholarly papers written about research with
reptiles, birds and small animals. He had also written
about one phase of heart trouble.

For a long time, Dr. Jenner wondered about the
relationship of cowpox to smallpox. Cowpox was a
disease that was common to dairy herds. The human
patients who most often contracted the disease were
milkmaids and dairymen who milked afflicted cows.
At the height of the disease the cow udder and teats
were covered with sores of running pus. The first

sign of the disease in the milker appeared as spots on the hands, then the disease spread over the skin and into the system. The disease was not unlike smallpox and country people claimed that no one would catch smallpox who had survived an attack of cowpox.

Smallpox was epidemic through the world, and in many lands the old wives' tale about cowpox was accepted by farmers and peasants. In China and some European countries attempts had been made to give cowpox to healthy people in the hope that mild cases of it might immunize them from smallpox. The myth and the crude methods for immunization had crossed to England where Jenner was in the right location to begin research.

Many of his patients had had cowpox so, as he traveled through the countryside, he slowly began to gather statistics. His statistics soon showed a definite pattern of answers to the questions he asked. Had the patient ever had cowpox? When? More than once? When the first answer was YES and the second answer, five years ago, or eight, or nineteen, then the third was always NO. After recovery all the questioned people had been exposed to cowpox many times but none had ever caught it twice.

Jenner confirmed his findings over and over again. He was extremely disturbed when he found that a

mother under his care was breast-feeding her baby
who had caught the disease from another child in
the family. When the mother didn't catch the disease
from either of her children, he asked whether she
had had cowpox. Of course. Twenty-seven years before when she herself was a toddler. Dr. Jenner's experience with patient after patient clearly indicated
to him that cowpox immunization against smallpox
was fact and permanent.

He decided on a bold plan for scientifically testing
his theory. He obtained the permission of the parents
of James Phipps, age nine, to inoculate their sturdy
son who was well and healthy. With a sharp scalpel,
Dr. Jenner made two slight cuts in the boy's skin. Pus
from a cowpox patient's sores was inserted into the
slight wound which was then bandaged. The next
day James' mouth was parched and dry, and he was
running a slight fever. The third and fourth day he
was a bit uncomfortable but not really sick. A small
sore, exposed when James' bandage was removed,
soon cleared up leaving a scar on the skin. The boy
did not contract cowpox.

Dr. Jenner repeated the experiment on James
twice again over a period of several months. The
reaction to the inoculation was the same and the result similar each time. The doctor was extremely
interested in one factor in the testing: the sore left

on James' skin was smaller and less infected after each successive experiment. Dr. Jenner interpreted that to mean that immunization was increased with each inoculation.

Jenner was elated. His theory was proved. Small-pox could be prevented by an inoculation method later called *vaccination,* a term based on the Latin word *vacca* meaning cow.

The modest country doctor was a good scientist who knew that continued research must follow even successful experimentation. He continued to vaccinate people, recording one hundred per cent immunization among those treated. Finally he found two people willing to cooperate in another drastic experiment. One of the test-humans he inoculated, the other he didn't. Both were then exposed to every possible situation in which cowpox might be contracted. The inoculated test-person did not catch the disease, the other one did.

It seems obvious that people who knew Dr. Jenner had great faith in him and his theory. They would hardly have risked their lives in experiments with a doctor whom they did not trust.

Dr. Jenner wrote a paper on his investigation of, and experiments with, cowpox and sent it for publication to the Royal Society of London. The paper was quickly returned with a stern letter from the

Society explaining they were doing him a favor by *not* publishing it. The Society warned that Dr. Jenner would expose himself to the ridicule of all scientists if he allowed the paper to be printed.

The normally mild-mannered and sweet-tempered Dr. Jenner was enraged by the high-handed attitude of the Society. In 1798, at his own expense, he published the paper which was entitled *An Inquiry into the Cause and Effects of the Variolae Vaccinae.*

Members of the Royal Society were astounded by his audacity and many of them condemned him for defying the Society. The reaction of other scientists and laymen was quite different. Physicians in France, hailing his research, began to vaccinate people in the hope of preventing smallpox epidemics. Catherine the Great of Russia urged doctors throughout her vast lands to protect her subjects by vaccination. The hard-headed, ruthless Napoleon did not suggest; he ordered that the soldiers of all his armies be vaccinated.

In America, Jenner's paper was read by Dr. Benjamin Waterhouse of Boston who vaccinated his own son in 1800. Thomas Jefferson, President of the United States, had his doctor vaccinate members of the Jefferson family and also his slaves and house servants at Monticello.

Acclaim for Jenner from so many leaders and respected professionals of Europe and America, quickly changed the attitude of his colleagues in England. Dr. Jenner received many honors, and funds for research were voted for him by the British Parliament. He was made Director of the National Vaccine Establishment. Shortly after he received a first grant of money from Parliament, Dr. Jenner went to London to practice medicine but he was unhappy in the big city. Within the year he returned to his village to resume his life as a country doctor.

We all owe a debt to Dr. Edward Jenner who had the vision to explore and investigate, to probe and prove a theory that has reduced smallpox to a sporadic disease. With brilliance and perseverance Dr. Jenner developed an idea which had increasing and ever-widening effects on medical science and its allied fields. As a result of his work millions of lives have been saved, millions of people have been spared the disfigurement of pockmarks left by smallpox.

Jenner's work was limited by the lack of clinical and biological knowledge, procedures and research equipment of his day. He demonstrated that smallpox could be prevented but he did not know why or how his inoculations worked. His method of direct transference of cowpox pus to skin incision was effective but rudimentary.

The understanding of immunization and tech-

niques of inoculation were established fifty years
after Jenner by Louis Pasteur, a scientist who well
deserves a place in the historic parade of men who
changed the world with their ideas.

Louis Pasteur, son of a tanner, was born in 1822 in
the small town of Dôle, in the Jura Department of
France. While a youngster, Louis showed no particular talent except for art, and his teachers were un-
impressed with his ability as a student. His outstanding characteristic was kindness to people and animals,
especially the ill, the deformed, the maimed, the
crippled. That quality of tenderness and compassion
was heightened in his later years of great achievement.

Pasteur's interest in scientific matters began when
he entered the College of Besançon in 1840. By the
time he received his Bachelor of Science degree in
1842, he was absorbed in the subject and was then
determined to work for a doctorate degree in chemistry at the Sorbonne in Paris. There Pasteur was influenced by several outstanding professors who were
enthusiastic about his potential ability, his acute
mind.

His scientific aptitude developed swiftly. Like
other men of genius he quickly absorbed the most
profound knowledge resulting from the work of his
predecessors. He turned promptly to research proj-

ects of his own and with impressive originality made an investigation of certain crystals and polarized light. Following the report of this research, scientists praised the outstanding contribution of Pasteur who was then only twenty-six.

With an enviable reputation established, Pasteur was appointed professor of physics at Dijon, went on to professorial posts first at Strasbourg, then at Lille where he was also dean of sciences. At Lille he produced research which catapulted him to international fame and involved him in the long-time controversy of *spontaneous generation.*

Lille was a center for the production of alcohol, and Pasteur was asked by alcohol processors to study the problem of wine that soured. He dropped his investigations of crystals and turned his attention to research in fermentation.

Most scientists, who had studied the problem of milk that curdled and wine that soured, believed unquestioningly that curdling and souring occurred spontaneously from some action, unknown and unidentified, within the liquid.

Pasteur doubted the spontaneous generation theory and set out to test it. After painstaking research, he announced that milk curdled and wine soured because of microorganisms floating free in the air—microorganisms which contaminated the liquid.

The tiny organisms, or germs, were not originally *in* the liquid, as other scientists had claimed.

With dramatic flourish Pasteur set up a demonstration to prove his point. He put equal amounts of liquid into an open laboratory beaker, and into a laboratory flask with only a small opening at the top. The wine in the wide-mouthed beaker soured; the wine in the flask was not affected because the organisms were trapped in the small opening and could not reach the liquid in the flask to contaminate it.

The practical work and scientific application of Pasteur exploded the spontaneous generation theory and established the fact that "germs" are in the air. Other scientists—including the outstanding German bacteriologist, Robert Koch—were following the germ-theory research in other conclusive directions.

Adversaries of the Pasteur theory were so scornful and harassed him so that Pasteur had to take time from research to debate with them and to demonstrate his experiments for them. The businessmen who ran the wine industries of France did not question Pasteur's word but accepted it as fact. Far from being scornful of his findings they turned to him for help in 1864 when wine production was being ruined in the area of Dôle, his birthplace.

At the urgent request of the wine producers threatened with the loss of fortunes, Pasteur set up a lab-

oratory in Jura. It was soon obvious that a microorganism, which was a devastating parasite, was get-
ting into the wine, causing it to sour. Pasteur, like
Newton, understood the importance of asking himself the right questions. In the Jura laboratory, he
queried: Can the parasitical microorganism be killed
by heating? If so, will the wine stand the heat? He
answered the questions by putting wine in beakers
and flasks that he placed over gas burners. The para-
sites were killed at between fifty and sixty degrees
Centigrade but the few minutes of heat did not
harm the wine.

Pasteur's success with wine led the French beer
barons to him. They were having problems with
great quantities of beer going sour in large vats. After
examining the spoiled beer, Pasteur said that a "microorganism foreign to the nature of true yeast" was
present in the liquid. Again he repeated the heat
process. Once more the offending microorganism was
destroyed, without changing the character or taste
of the liquid—in this case, beer.

Sterilization of liquids to prevent fermentation was
referred to as *pasteurization* in honor of the man who
developed the process. The importance of the work
has changed the world in which milk is labeled *Pas-
teurized,* signifying that the healthful liquid is safe
to drink, germ-free.

It was natural that a man as humane and kindly as Pasteur should turn his scientific attention to disease. Having established his germ theory, he was convinced that he must find a way to isolate the germs which caused certain diseases. He knew about Jenner's work with inoculation and about the advances made since Jenner's time. Pasteur's investigations centered first on *anthrax,* a disease that afflicted cows and sheep. Anthrax caused lesions on the skin, enlargement of the spleen, and a quick weakening of the entire body. The disease was nearly always fatal, so a farmer was likely to be wiped out almost overnight when his herd or flock was struck with anthrax.

Economic disaster also was brought on by epidemics of chicken cholera. This disease often swept through poultry farms at great loss to owners.

Pasteur spent five years studying anthrax and chicken cholera. He was able to isolate the germ, the bacillus which caused each disease. He also found ways to store the germs for future use in immunization. His methods and procedures extended Jenner's pioneering work with inoculation.

Following Jenner's theory, Pasteur discovered that he could inject healthy sheep with small doses of the *anthrax bacillus* and healthy chickens with the chicken cholera *virus* without infecting the sheep or chickens with the respective diseases which would have swept through the flock. Test after test showed that sheep could be protected from anthrax and poultry from chicken cholera. Not content with this remarkable progress, Pasteur refined the technique by repeatedly experimenting with varying germ-strength inoculations. Incidentially, he named the inoculation process *vaccination* in honor of Jenner's *variolae vaccinae*.

When Pasteur's findings were definite enough to suit him, he decided to forestall the sort of ridicule and scorn which had followed his announcement of the germ theory. The Melun Agricultural Society of France gave Pasteur a herd of sheep, sixty animals. He ran tests on a few of the sheep and then announced that he would give a public demonstration of the value of vaccination on May 31. The year was 1881.

Under the supervision of members of the Society Pasteur had vaccinated twenty-four sheep of the herd with isolated anthrax bacillus. On the day of the demonstration, the vaccinated sheep were put into one pasture, twenty-four unvaccinated sheep in a separate fenced area. Pasteur injected all forty-eight of the sheep with strong anthrax cultures.

Two days later the vaccinated sheep were healthy and strong as they grazed on tender pasture grass. The twenty-four unvaccinated sheep were dead or dying from anthrax. Scientists, newspaper men, farmers and all others who had gathered for the demonstration were convinced that Pasteur's vaccination was effective.

He accepted his honors with modesty and returned to work. The next indicated step was to apply the technique of germ isolation to human beings. With quiet determination Pasteur tackled the terrible disease: rabies. Rabies was transmitted directly from mad dogs to unfortunate victims. Mad dogs, frothing at the mouth and running wild, in their frenzy bit people who more often than not died in agony from the contracted rabies.

Pasteur studied the salivary froth from the mouths of rabid dogs and found no germs, no substance which could be injected to induce rabies in other dogs. He decided that the "mad" actions of the rabid dogs indicated that the nervous system was the key to the solution he sought. With his usual calm precision, Pasteur took bits of tissue from the spinal cord at the base of the brain and injected the cultures into healthy dogs who became mad.

Laboriously Pasteur continued experiments until he found a way to secure a large supply of the virus. He injected rabbits with virus from mad dogs and the rabbits died. Then he injected this virus from dead rabbits into other rabbits until he had enough virus to inject into dogs. The vaccination of dogs continued through many experimental inoculations until it was quite certain that the treatment did successfully prevent rabies. Pasteur's discovery was acclaimed but his ultimate goal was not reached. He wanted to cure people who had been bitten by mad dogs.

His opportunity to test his rabies technique on a human being came on July 6, 1885. Three people were brought to the Pasteur laboratory: Theodore Vone, a grocer, had been scratched by his own dog that had gone mad; Joseph Meister, a nine-year-old boy, who had been ferociously attacked by Monsieur Vone's dog; and the boy's mother. The boy had several deep, tooth-torn wounds that bled profusely.

Here was the patient Pasteur had been waiting for, but the prospect of trying the inoculation was emotionally upsetting. Pasteur sent the grocer home assuring him that he would not contract the disease. The boy was kept at the laboratory. No one knew what would happen if the boy was given injections of the virus of rabies. It was certain that without treatment he would die the horrible, torturing death resulting from the disease.

After asking the advice of several doctors, Pasteur courageously started the injections sixty hours after the boy had been bitten. He gave young Joseph thirteen injections in ten days. Pasteur sat by the patient's bed almost continually. He slept little and ate hardly at all. As time went by Pasteur became physically and emotionally exhausted. Gradually his hopes were raised. Each day the boy seemed to improve. Finally, after the thirteenth injection it seemed that the battle was won. The boy was well.

Pasteur left for a country holiday to calm his nerves and regain the physical strength he had lost during the ordeal. For months afterward Pasteur kept a close watch on the Meister boy, fearing that there might be a relapse, a flare-up of the disease. Pasteur's fears were groundless. The boy was cured.

Word of Pasteur's triumph over rabies spread. Other patients rushed to his laboratory. Veterinarians and physicians secured supplies of the virus which they used to inoculate healthy animals and to cure people bitten by rabid dogs.

Pasteur was a creative humanitarian who enthusiastically approached any scientific problem that would contribute to the physical or economic well-being of his fellow-men. It was typical that Pasteur's greatest feats in science—isolation of microorganisms, destruction of microorganisms, prevention and mitigation of disease by vaccination—were accomplishments that benefited man and the world in which he lives.

Polish-born scientist who discovered radium, while
working in France, and died from the gift she gave
to mankind.

MARIE CURIE, 1867-1934

SINCE man produced the first primitive
flame of fire, woman has stirred bubbling liquids in
pots set over heat. Through the ages and in all civilizations, it has been customary for women to be busy
with the domestic chore of cooking. But the unique
example of a woman who labored over hot kettles
day in and day out from 1898 to 1902 is recorded not
in cookbooks but in histories of science.

The woman was Marie Curie and her kettles, huge
as witches' caldrons, contained no edible mixture.
What she stirred and separated and processed produced a new element which was to save many lives
and cause her own death.

Marie Curie was born Marie Sklodowska on No-
vember 7, 1867, in Warsaw, Poland. Her parents were
both school teachers who actively worked with under-
ground groups trying to counteract the influences

which had come through the partition of Poland in
the eighteenth century. Oppressive Czarist overlords
insisted that Russian should be the official language
in schools and sent inspectors to be sure that courses,
especially of history and language, were taught according to Russian standards.

The little girl, brought up in a home with books
and lively discussions on education, proved at an
early age that she was exceedingly bright. At five she
could read in her native language, Polish. At ten she
could read German, French and Russian, and passed
advanced tests in mathematics, history and literature.

She wasn't just a bookish child, however. Many of
her relatives lived in the country where she learned
to be an expert horsewoman and to take part in all
sorts of sports. She loved to go to parties and often
danced until dawn with partners who were charmed
by her gaiety, her infectious smile.

Her family had a financial struggle after her father
lost his teaching job in 1873 because he deliberately
had not followed the strict curriculum set up by the
Russians. There was no money to send Marie's sister,
Bronya, to medical school in Paris. Since no women
were allowed in the Polish universities, any girl who
wanted to get an advanced education had to go to
another country, a condition which both of the sisters
resented.

Marie, who had been well educated by her father, insisted on becoming a governess so she could financially help Bronya, the family's medical student. While Marie taught ABCs and other elementary subjects to the children of wealthy parents, she read every available book and pamphlet on science subjects. For a time she joined a group of young Polish patriots who set up a secret laboratory where they could experiment with new ideas, could instruct each other in subjects they had studied in what really was a "floating university." The students held informal meetings in various homes and halls that substituted for classrooms.

By 1891, Marie had enough money to go to Paris to study at the Sorbonne. She lived in a sparsely furnished attic room and studied in university libraries which were warmer than her chilly garret. She spent only a few cents a day on food and lost weight but she gained enormous amounts of knowledge.

Her professors were amazed and delighted with the achievements of the slim Polish girl. By 1893 she topped the list of brilliant candidates for the degree of Master of Arts in Physics. A year later she was praised by scholars when she won her degree of Master of Arts in Mathematics.

A physicist friend thought she might like to talk about a proposed research project with a French scientist, noted for his work in crystallography and magnetism. The Frenchman was a shy bachelor in his mid-thirties. His name was Pierre Curie. Over tea he and Marie talked science and he was enchanted by the beautiful young woman with the brilliant mind.

Ten months after their first meeting Marie and Pierre were married. They began a life in which they were personally happy and a scientific collaboration which produced revolutionary results. They worked on complex problems of physics, using daring and unorthodox methods to solve those problems.

The background for their scientific thinking which changed our world was provided by two of their contemporaries, Wilhelm Roentgen, a German physicist, and Henri Becquerel, a French mineralogist. In 1895 Roentgen discovered X rays. These invisible electromagnetic radiations of high frequency when passed through human beings or through inanimate objects could be made to cast a shadow of organs and bones of the body, of the structure of the mass.

Becquerel, like all other scientists, was excited by Roentgen's discovery and wanted to know more about results that could be obtained through the X ray. He saw that X rays beamed on glass produced a fluorescence, a glow, and noticed how they affected sensitive photographic paper. His curiosity led him to wonder whether all fluorescent specimens affected photographic paper.

With care he wrapped many fluorescent specimens in black paper, put the packages beside photographic paper in an inky-black room. Some specimens exposed the paper, others did not. Becquerel excitedly continued his research. He tested every specimen that exposed the photographic paper and found that each contained uranium. Probing deeper into the phenomenon, he learned that uranium continues to give off energy, radiates particles of some kind of energy with continuing power.

Becquerel had made an outstanding contribution to science but he was not aware of its full significance. As a matter of fact, he stopped working with the phenomenon after his initial research. However, he talked at length about his project with his friends, the Curies, and Marie wanted to continue the project and to make it the subject of her doctoral thesis.

With a combination of creative imagination and realistic research she submitted uranium ore to many different scientific tests. Repeating her experiments over and over again, checking one kind of test with still another, she proved that the intensity of radiation from a specimen of uranium ore was exactly proportionate to the amount of uranium in the ore. With astonishing mathematical precision she showed that the radiation came from the atoms of uranium.

Her conclusion led her to another question: If uranium emits energy are there other elements which do the same thing? She selected thorium as her next test-element. The thorium atoms also emitted energy and the active radiations continued to throw off strong rays.

With proven facts about two elements Marie Curie announced that certain elements had what she called *radioactivity.* She coined the word which is such a familiar one today and started an entire new area in chemical and physical science. Becquerel recognized the existence of radioactivity but Marie Curie, with the invaluable assistance of her husband, Pierre, dedicated her thinking and her life to the study of radioactive elements.

Reports of her investigations were circulated among European scientists who indicated their deep respect for this remarkable young woman by the very way they referred to her or addressed her as *Madame* Curie. She could have accepted the praise and relaxed after her early achievements. Instead she graciously acknowledged the compliments of colleagues and hurried back to her makeshift workroom that served as laboratory. She continued to examine scores of previously untested minerals.

Imagine her excitement when she found that the

mineral *pitchblende* had a radioactive emission four times greater than that of uranium. With precision she separated the known elements in pitchblende. To her astonishment not one of the known elements was radioactive. She came to the only possible conclusion: pitchblende must contain one or more elements unknown to scientists.

Pierre Curie had become so absorbed in his wife's research that he gave up his own work on crystals and magnetism. Together, using every known method of chemical analysis, they isolated a new element from pitchblende. Madame Curie called it *polonium* in honor of the land where she was born.

Again the Curies began to analyze the pitchblende in the hope of finding a second unknown element. This time they found *radium,* a word that became almost a term of magic in laboratories of pure research; in sciences including physics, chemistry, biology and medicine; and in industry.

The element radium when first identified by the Curies could not be weighed on a scale; it was a mere speck. Radium is less than one-millionth of a part of pitchblende. No wonder it was unknown before the patient, untiring Curies had started their search by chemical analysis.

In order to produce a measurable amount of radium, it was necessary to have tremendous amounts of pitchblende, a substance that is a waste material of uranium mining. It is as dirty as soft coal. The Curies ordered tons of pitchblende and set to work as a team. Pierre Curie analyzed the physical properties of radium. Madame Curie went to work with her kettles.

They put the kettles in an old shack which was hot in summer and cold in winter, and damp during rain or snow. There, in unpleasant surroundings, Marie Curie dumped pitchblende into vats where it melted and boiled. She stirred through exhausting days. For four miserable years the Curies labored to extract small amounts of radium from tons and tons of pitchblende. Finally, in 1902, the Curies had one three-hundredth of an ounce of pure radium! This fluorescent element gave off intense rays and steady heat.

Scientists throughout the world eagerly awaited the arrival of the professional journals in which the Curies' scientific feat was reported. Research scholars in laboratories recognized that radioactivity was the possible key to many kinds of scientific investigation. Scientists from everywhere journeyed to Paris to talk to the Curies, to learn about the new element. Scientific societies on the continent and in England invited the Curies to lecture on their discovery.

In 1903 the Nobel Prize in Physics was awarded

to Henri Becquerel, to Pierre and Marie Curie, three people responsible for a revolution in science made possible by recognition of the phenomenon of radioactivity and the discovery of radium.

Uses for radium began to be applied in many places, in a number of ways. The potentially lethal rays of radium were being tested in the treatment of the dread disease of cancer. Studies of radioactivity were radically changing the concepts of atomic structure and the basic nature of chemical reactions.

Vast new frontiers of chemistry and physics were opening up but the Curies continued to work without a suitable laboratory. Both Pierre and Marie, like her parents a generation before, had to teach to live. Finally in 1904 they received the funds from the Nobel Prize which eased their economic condition and they looked forward to productive years of research together.

Those plans and future hopes ended one afternoon in 1906 when Pierre was tragically killed in a Paris street accident. That shock changed Madame Curie who never regained her gaiety of spirit. But sorrow in no way affected her dedication to her scientific work; if anything that was intensified after her husband's death.

She continued to work with radium and radioactivity. She deserved the fame and adulation that has come to few people and to no other woman scientist before her. In 1911, for the extraction of radium, she again was given the Nobel Prize, the only person to have been twice honored by that award.

The Institute of Radium in Paris was founded in her honor and so was a similar institute in Warsaw, her birthplace. At the Paris Institute, as director of fundamental research, she was able to extend her influence through scholars who flocked to her from all over the world.

The Curies had two daughters, Irène who was a toddler during the kettle-stirring days, and Ève born shortly after her parents won the Nobel Prize. Following the death of her husband, Madame Curie devoted her personal life to the daughters. Ève became a writer and the biographer of her famous mother. Irène became a scientist and like her mother married a scientist, Frédéric Joliot.

Irène and Frédéric worked as scientific collaborators in the Curie tradition. They discovered the neutron of the atom and produced artificial radioactivity. For their work they received the Nobel Prize in Chemistry in 1935.

Unfortunately, Madame Curie did not live to see them honored. Although her years of close work with the deadly rays of radium had resulted in skin burns that left her scarred, she did not fully understand the need for vigilant protection against the rays. Constant bombardment of radium rays finally so weakened her blood that it was impossible for her body to manufacture red corpuscles fast enough. Madame Curie died of pernicious anemia, a disease brought on by radium, the element she gave to the world.

British Nobel prize-winning scientists whose work gave new direction to all areas of contemporary science through their discoveries in atomic physics.

FREDERICK SODDY, 1877-1956
ERNEST RUTHERFORD, 1871-1937

THROUGH ages of history man has known the name but not the nature of an atom. It is possible that even scientists of ancient Greece gave some thought to indivisible particles of matter, particles too minute to see, too infinitesimal to divide. One reason for believing that such particles were of interest to ancient Greeks is that the word for the smallest particle of matter is *atom* which in Greek means indivisible. And in scientific history atom is the one word by which the indivisible particle has been designated.

"Smashing the atom," a term familiar enough today, was not only unknown but unthinkable a hundred years ago. The actual breakthrough of the components of the atom was made by two scientists, trained in England, Ernest Rutherford and Frederick Soddy.

Ernest Rutherford was born in New Zealand on August 20, 1871, the fourth of twelve children whose father was a wheelwright and flax miller. Even as a boy Rutherford had a compelling personality. His lively nature was reflected in bright blue eyes, and he talked rapidly in an incessant loud voice. His body, large and powerful, was strengthened by farm work, by active participation in sports. He was above average as a student and did so well in school that he had plenty of time for outside interests, one of which was science.

At Nelson College and at the University of New Zealand, he set the pattern of his work life. He slept few hours at night because he could doze off for refreshing catnaps during the day. He was ever an indefatigable worker and exhausted his colleagues in science by trying to force them to keep going at his rapid pace.

Rutherford left the University of New Zealand and went to England where he studied at Cambridge with Sir Joseph John Thomson, a British Nobel-prize physicist, whose many contributions to science included discovery of the electron. Inspired by Sir Joseph, Rutherford plunged into studies of the atom to which he devoted his mind and vast energies for the rest of his life.

Frederick Soddy, born in Eastbourne, England, September 2, 1877, also came from a family of modest means. Unlike Rutherford, Soddy was slight, wiry, and quiet in manner. He attended Eastbourne College and then went up to Oxford University where he, too, became interested in the study of the atom. Although Soddy was a brilliant and meticulous researcher, he did not give his full attention to science as Rutherford did. Soddy was equally interested in social reform, and in later years formulated a theory of importance not to science but in the field of economics. It had to do with monetary matters, not physical matter.

The atom research done by Rutherford with Soddy was carried on in Montreal, Canada, when both men were professors at McGill University.

Before we look at their work, it is necessary to highlight some scientific discoveries which made possible their research. Those advances in science date from Benjamin Franklin whose experiments with a kite proved the identity of lightning and electricity. He was followed by Alessandro Volta who developed a device for producing electric charges by induction; the standard unit of electromotive force, the volt, was named for the Italian physicist. A contemporary of his was the British chemist and physicist, Sir Humphry Davy, whose electrochemical research, along with the work of Volta, influenced Michael Faraday. He too was a British scientist of major reputation, partially earned through his discovery of electromagnetic induction.

It was John Dalton, a remarkable but untrained scientific thinker, who, in the early nineteenth century, made original observations on the subject of weight of matter as influenced by atoms. Amadeo Avogadro's annotations about atom and molecule, and the electromagnetic waves produced and studied by Heinrich Hertz, added to the total information assembled before Rutherford and Soddy began their research. The two scientists who teamed up at McGill also had available to them the studies resulting from three major discoveries: X ray by Wilhelm Roentgen; radioactivity by Henri Becquerel and the Curies, Pierre and Marie; and radium, then being experimented with by the Curies.

It is essential to point out that many of the discoveries and developments on which the Rutherford –Soddy work was dependent were unintentional aids to that research. Franklin, Faraday, Volta and other scientists could not have known that facts and techniques they found and developed would be tools for atomic research.

Information about, and knowledge of, the atom

grew gradually. Curiosity about the atom stimulated many late nineteenth-century scientists on several counts. There were so many unknowns, including the very cause and nature of radioactivity.

Rutherford was one of the scientists determined to explain the causes of radioactivity. From experiments with radium and uranium he found what he called *alpha particles* and *beta particles*. The alpha rays were slower and less penetrating than the beta rays which were not quickly absorbed in the air but were high-speed and penetrating.

A year after his findings on the rays, Rutherford began his Canadian studies with Soddy. For two years they worked in their laboratory constantly, unceasingly studying atoms. In 1902 they reported that certain *atoms were unstable and that instability caused the spontaneous disintegration of those atoms.* These thirteen words seem so simple when read today. In the early part of the century, the words created a revolution in atomic science and gave new direction to all areas of modern science because they established the existence of atomic energy.

Rutherford returned to England to teach and to continue his research at the University of Manchester. There he made another astounding discovery. Basing his experiments on the principle of radioactive disintegration, he found that an atom was centered with a positively charged nucleus made up mostly of positively charged protons with a few neutrons, around which negatively charged electrons revolved. The negative electrons balanced in exact numbers the positive protons in the nucleus, making the whole atom neutral.

That discovery was immeasurably important and Rutherford was awarded a Nobel Prize for it in 1908. Five years later, Niels Bohr, the Danish physicist who won the 1922 Nobel Prize for his concept of atom structure, correlated Rutherford's nuclear theory with the quantum theory of energy. That research established the "model" of the atom that remains the foundation for today's increasing developments in many fields of peacetime atomic applications.

Rutherford intensified his research when he became head of the Cavendish Laboratory at Cambrige. Again working with a collaborator, Professor Chadwick, later Sir James Chadwick, he demonstrated that an atomic element could be artificially disintegrated, that man himself could trigger and release the power confined in atoms. The atoms thus set off would not only explode but at the same time would create new energy.

At Oxford University, Frederick Soddy continued his studies of atomic fission and with the British chemist, Ramsay (Sir William Ramsay), proved that helium could be produced from the fission, or splitting, of radium; that one element could be made from another!

Even while working separately, Rutherford and Soddy continued to expand the science of atomic physics by concentrating on the same area of research: the isotope. Rutherford theorized that certain elements exist in two or more forms that have different weights, but are not chemically recognizable. He proved his theory by precise experimentation that revealed recognition of the forms, the differences between the atoms of the same element, and permitted measurement by weight.

The atom–isotope relationship is complex. In general broad terms the major idea can be understood by accepting the fact that atoms of most elements exist in two forms which can be called *common atoms* and *isotopes*. The two forms are chemically alike but differ in weight.

The isotope itself is of two kinds: *stable* and *unstable*. The stable isotope, as its name indicates, remains fixed. The unstable isotope disintegrates. It throws off bits of itself in the form of radioactive rays and eventually the invisible unstable isotope is broken up. The rays, which can be detected by a Geiger counter, are at once deadly and valuable.

The unstable isotope is dangerous if uncontrolled because it can destroy living tissue. But that very property makes the unstable isotope useful in arresting or curing some diseases.

For example, it is known that certain chemicals go to specific parts of the human body. Iodine, if taken into the body, goes straight to the thyroid gland. Knowing this fact, doctors have successfully experimented with treatments of thyroid disorders by feeding radioactive iodine to patients through the mouth. The iodine isotopes bombard or destroy certain tissues so that a patient is cured or relieved by the controlled treatment.

The radioactive rays of the unstable isotope are used in agriculture as tracing agents of real worth. Elements in food-producing plants can be traced with a Geiger counter through roots, stems, leaves, flowers and fruit or vegetable. By such testing, crops can be controlled through the study of the experiment-results. Animal diseases can be cut down through similar isotopic research.

Since the radioactive rays thrown off by unstable isotopes can penetrate inanimate objects, as well as living things, industry uses the isotopes for testing the strength and uniformity of manufactured products. The unstable isotope has many uses in medicine, biology, industry, and its usefulness increases almost daily. The present applications of isotopic properties probably would astound Rutherford and Soddy who revealed the presence of the isotope and established the facts of its nature. It was their research that made it possible for other scientists to extend the understanding of, and increase the uses for, this phenomenon.

The original research by Rutherford and Soddy at McGill influenced and set the direction for their separate investigations in later years. In 1932, Ernest Rutherford, then Lord Rutherford, experimentally split the atom. His atomic research at Cambridge was continuous until his death in 1937.

Frederick Soddy was awarded the Nobel Prize in Chemistry in 1921 as a result of collaborative research in radioactivity that led to his theory of isotopes. Eventually he withdrew slowly from the world of science. He became almost a recluse and spent his time writing about economics, monetary reforms and social problems. He died at the age of seventy-nine in 1956.

Earlier we pointed out that these two giants of science were able to revolutionize science because of knowledge made available by the work of scientists who preceded them. That fact should not detract from their genius. As vast new areas of science are uncovered they become points of departure for remarkable discoveries by imaginative, creative scientists.

Rutherford—energetic, robust and dynamic—had an incredible talent for thinking up and performing the exact experiment with which to prove one of his specific theoretical ideas. Soddy—withdrawn and reflective—was able to think through a subject until he arrived at an exact theory that would pinpoint a crucial fact.

It would be wrong to call these two scientists the fathers of modern atomic science. It is correct to hail them as the two men who set off the chain reaction of modern atomic science which has so radically changed our world.

German neurologist who courageously contradicted his colleagues and founded the science of psychoanalysis.

SIGMUND FREUD, 1856-1939

MISERY and torture used to be the lot of most people with troubled minds. Crazy, mad, daft were words used to describe those who suffered from mental illness or from psychosomatic sickness of the type recognized today as a physical ailment induced by emotional or mental disturbances.

The plight of these pitiful people was explained, through the ages, by countless superstitions: they were possessed by devils. They were being punished by the gods for wrongdoing, or for the sins of their parents. Ignorant beliefs in many variations multiplied for centuries.

Even in the early 1800s, supposedly intelligent men and women considered it a lark to visit insane asylums where they laughed gaily at the awful involuntary antics of patients chained in filthy rooms. Cruel friends and relatives enjoyed poking fun at the mentally disturbed who frequently were dragged into drawing rooms for the amusement of guests at a party. Fortunately the mentally ill are no longer treated like criminals or clowns. Enlightenment about illnesses of the mind began in the eighteenth century when a few medical men began to study the human mind, to investigate the nervous system. From their efforts the science of neurology gradually evolved.

Philippe Pinel, a French neurologist, was one of the serious men of science who believed that the initial step toward curing the mentally ill should be to release them from chains. In 1792, Pinel published a book about his own first, faltering efforts to understand the unfortunate creatures who always had been shockingly mistreated. His important publication stressed that understanding should begin with human kindness, gentleness and abolishment of the indignities to which the mentally ill had been subjected.

Other scientists followed the lead of Pinel or on their own tried to discover ways for curing those with slightly troubled minds, aiding those who seemed hopelessly demented. Some doctors, including the famous physician Benjamin Rush of Philadelphia, suggested drugs to counteract mental disturbances. Small successes were achieved, multiple failures recorded.

During the latter part of the nineteenth century,

one man developed an approach to the subject which brought about a radical change in man's observation of human behavior, of himself. Through new ideas man was forced to see himself in a new light, to an understanding of why he acts the way he does. The doctor who presented the revolutionary and controversial ideas was Sigmund Freud.

Sigmund Freud was born on May 6, 1856, in the town of Freiberg, Germany. He is referred to now as a Viennese doctor because his family moved to Austria when he was four years old. The sensitive and gentle boy grew up to be a quiet, kindly man whose theories rocked the world and created an impact not only in the fields of medicine and mental health but also in the arts: literature, drama, music, ballet, painting and sculpture.

Early in life Freud showed a real aptitude for science. As a schoolboy he was influenced and stimulated by the progressive and scholarly research being done in Vienna, then one of the world's science centers. He first was captivated by botany and chemistry and spent his time reading comprehensively about those subjects and experimenting in a laboratory. An intense interest in medicine developed as Freud studied and he began to specialize in neurology, the science of nervous disorders. This background in neurology won for him an appointment at the Institute of Cerebral Anatomy where, with other doctors, he worked with patients who were drug addicts.

At the Institute, Freud saw men and women ravaged mentally, physically, morally by the use of drugs. While trying to effect cures, Freud began to wonder why people took to drugs. What experience, what tragedy, what action drove people to addiction? The reasons, he believed, had to be emotional or mental.

Dr. Josef Breuer, a colleague, told Freud about successes with hypnosis of patients. Breuer would hypnotize a patient who was hysterical and psychoneurotic and then would ask the patient questions about the past, about fears, shocks and phobias, and about unhappy experiences. Breuer explained to Freud that he often had been able to help people understand their problems by relating those problems to things the patient had said while under hypnosis.

The hypnosis technique and Breuer's results captured Freud's interest and he began to work with Breuer. The association continued for some years and, in 1893, Breuer and Freud published a book, setting forth the results of their collaboration, giving case histories of treatment of patients under hypnotic spells.

Eventually Freud decided to do away with hypnosis and to talk directly with patients in a conscious state. He started on a path of independent research which was to be a lonely trail. Patiently and tirelessly he questioned patients who were physically ill. He won their confidence and led them to talk about their lives. In time the patients would dredge out of the past long-forgotten incidents that seemed to have been buried deep in their minds, incidents that they had totally forgotten. Some of the remembered-experiences went back to the patients' childhood days.

Freud suspected that hidden memories, too painful to recall, had a correlation with physical illness. He found that once the memories were brought out and discussed, a patient's physical condition very often improved. Unknown to the patient there seemed to be an energy, long-buried somewhere within him, that aggravated or caused illness.

Turning from the physically ill to the mentally ill, Freud continued investigations based on his wide experience with many patients. He used the same study-technique: quiet questioning, gentle encouragement to say whatever came to mind. Gradually through the years, Freud evolved a theory of psychoanalysis, advanced a new concept of human behavior, developed methods for treating the mentally ill.

It took years for Freud to come to the conclusions accepted today by doctors who follow Freudian concepts and techniques.

One of Freud's first theories stated that the mind was divided between the conscious and the unconscious. Unpleasant, terrifying, frightening, unhappy experiences, dating from the day of birth, went into the unconscious mind. There the experiences were caged, imprisoned and prevented from flowing into daily thought, the conscious part of the mind. The rigidity of the division caused a conflict between the reality of the conscious mind and the unreality of the unconscious mind. That conflict, Freud believed early in his research, provided the basis for many kinds of neurotic, mental disturbances.

For many years Freud tested theory after theory retaining some, rejecting others, like the original one on the conflict of the conscious and the unconscious. Gradually through several stages he moved closer to his final concept of the human mind and how it works, how and why it becomes troubled.

Freud eventually recognized that there was a problem, deeply rooted in childhood, which he called the Oedipus complex. The complex develops when a boy's love for his mother becomes so strong that he turns against his father; when a girl's love for her father becomes so strong that she turns against her mother. The situation usually is an unconscious one so the boy or girl does not know how or why it comes about, or does not even realize that the complex exists.

Nevertheless it is present in the mind and guides the actions and attitudes of the boy or girl. Generally when the child grows to adulthood, the complex disappears and no harm is done. Sometimes, however, the complex remains so strong that it produces neurosis.

The term *Oedipus complex* was adopted by Freud from the ancient Greek myth about Oedipus. When Oedipus was born the prediction was made that the baby would grow up and kill his father and marry his mother. Because of the dire warning by a soothsayer, the infant Oedipus was sent away and reared without knowledge of his parents, who they were or where they lived. While wandering in Greece as a young man, Oedipus met and killed the king of Thebes, who in reality was his father. The king's murderer went to Thebes and there the conqueror Oedipus married the queen, Jocasta, who was his mother. Oedipus suffered through his life when he learned the truth of his actions: he had hated his enemy the king of Thebes and had loved his mother, Jocasta.

Freud adopted the highly overdrawn mythical case as illustration for describing a moderate psychological situation which sometimes unconsciously exists between children and parents. The situation, when acute, can create mental disturbances.

Freud did not state, nor did he believe, that this was the only cause of neurosis but he described it simply as one of many problems of sexual adjustment a child has to make in the process of growing up.

While seeking to find the mental mechanism which might cause psychological problems, Freud finally assigned to the mind three regions: the *id,* the *ego,* and the *super ego.* These form the basis of Freudian psychology for understanding the mind and its problems, and the approaches for cure of mental illness of many degrees and kinds.

He described the *id* as the natural instinct with which people are born; as the part of the mind that is inherited, present at birth and fixed. Here, according to Freud, is the carefree, uninhibited part of the mind that seeks pleasure and action without restrictions of any kind.

The *ego* he described as that portion of the mind which must face the external realities of the world as the human grows up; which must learn to control the natural instincts, must try to cope with the restrictions of the world in which the human being lives. The *ego* can be partially termed the conscience of a person.

The *super ego* is that third region of the mind which results from the rules and laws enforced by parents, representing the first authority which grants affection and threatens punishment if rules and laws are broken. In later life the *super ego* is influenced by teachers, by leaders of all kinds, and by an ever-increasing number of external laws (regulations and social patterns) imposed on the mind.

It is necessary to understand the three areas which Freud said were the basic mechanisms by which the mind works and which control the thoughts and actions of people.

Freud did not say that the three areas are sharply defined, rigidly separated one from another. He clearly said that the *id,* the *ego* and *super ego* shade slowly from one into the other. Furthermore he did not say that one region was always in control. Instead, he was sure that the relative dominance of any one of the regions over the others varies from person to person, and with any given person from time to time.

Nevertheless, Freud firmly believed that obvious conflicts among the three regions of the mind are the basis for mental disturbances. Conflicts arise when the *id,* the natural instinct, demands an action that is rejected or sublimated by the *ego,* the human conscience, and/or the *super ego.* To some degree, at different times this battle goes on within the minds of all human beings. Sometimes the battle is so strong that constant *repression,* the holding down of the *id,* creates violent mental disturbances, or at least an unhappy mental condition.

With this understanding of the mental mechanism, Freud stated that a psychoanalyst, by constantly searching and probing into the human mind, can help a patient to remember long-forgotten experiences and incidents causing the conflict within the mind. When the reason for the conflict is found, the psychoanalyst can help the patient understand the cause, can begin to guide the patient toward a cure.

In order to discover the cause and source of the conflict the patient talks endlessly to the doctor in what is termed *free association,* the discussion of anything which comes to the patient's mind. When this is done over a long enough period both analyst and patient probe deeper into the mind and bring to light the cause of the disturbance.

As Freud's theories became widely known and his techniques were practiced by him and other doctors, a storm of disapproval swept around him. He was taunted, called vile names and ridiculed by most people. Controversy about his theories and methods continues today. Since his time many details of Freud's work have been changed. Many of his theories have been further developed as psychologists and psychiatrists come closer to an understanding of the most elusive portion of the human body—the mind.

New methods, based on chemical reasons for neurosis, have been advanced and are being studied. New methods of mental therapy have been devised. New-found facts extend the ideas of Freud.

Today even opponents of Freudian theories admit that his research, his probing, his ideas about the mechanism of the mind were truly revolutionary. Freud's work made all medical men, psychologists and neurologists direct their studies toward the basis of human motivation. His work gave scientists a whole new perspective from which to view human actions, problems, cures.

He accomplished more than that. Freud's contributions created such an impact on society that writers used his concepts as the basis for fiction motivation, in novels, plays and short stories. Painters and sculptors were affected by Freudian theories and many new forms of art were created because of his idea. His terminology quickly found its way into daily conversation. Masses of people for the first time began to consider their own personal actions in a new light, with new understanding.

Problems of the human mind are among the most baffling faced by the medical profession. Today physicians constantly continue to explore in the fields of mental health and mental illness. They credit that pioneer, Sigmund Freud, with studies of the mind and its influence on the whole body that changed our world because they changed the way man looks at himself.

German-American theoretical physicist, founder of the theory of relativity, whose ideas brought into being our modern age of atomic energy.

ALBERT EINSTEIN, 1879-1955

IN 1895, Albert Einstein started to think about a complex subject that produced the first germ of his ultimate theory of relativity. He was only sixteen years old.

At an earlier age Einstein was considered a poor student because he disliked having to learn and to memorize routine facts that he would be required to write by rote on examination papers. In school he was neither popular nor a good student. He was a solitary and silent boy who stayed to himself reading all kinds of books not used in schools for young pupils his age. He read books on nature, physics, history and social problems, delving into subjects aimlessly, seemingly without purpose until he found one set of volumes: *Peoples Books on Natural History.* Their pages opened an entire new world to Albert. He was excited by what Aaron Bernstein had written about natural history, and the words awakened his naturally brilliant mind. Here at last that spark fired his imagination and roused interest as schoolboy lessons had failed to do.

Einstein was born on March 14, 1879, in Ulm, Germany, but he spent his childhood in Munich where his German-Jewish parents moved in 1880. His mother shared music with him and encouraged him to take violin lessons. Each year as Einstein grew, he spent more time alone and seemed increasingly lost in thoughts of his own. Simple arithmetic never captured young Albert's attention but he thrilled to mathematics when an uncle taught him the rudiments of that science. His own studies of history made him increasingly religious and proud of being a Jew, and more eager to probe the meaning and depths of the faith of his people.

Einstein's father decided to move the family from Munich to Italy but Albert, although he was only in his early teens, refused to go. He moved instead to Aarau, Switzerland, and worked there at various odd jobs while he continued his studies. At sixteen he became curious about the speed of light, a subject that posed many hypothetical questions for him. One of the questions that he asked himself about the motion of light was: If you could be on the front of a wave of light moving through space, would you have the feeling of being in motion? His answer was negative because the person at the front of the light wave would seem to be in the same place all the time, or to be stationary. You can follow the simplification of Einstein's reasoning by first imagining yourself at the front of the light wave, and then by imagining that you are looking at someone else at the front of the light wave. Observing from a distance you would see that the other person was in motion, was moving with the wave of light. In other words, as Einstein decided, all things are relative depending on the point of view of the observer.

In 1896, he entered the Zurich Polytechnic Institute where as usual the dull routine of classroom work bored him. Again he studied independently, reading chiefly the scholarly works of famous scientists like Maxwell, Helmholtz, Hertz and Kirchhoff. With a few people who shared his specific interests Einstein talked fluently and earnestly but he stayed mostly to himself.

He became a Swiss citizen in 1900 and five years later, after being awarded his Ph.D. degree, looked in vain for a teaching post. Failing in his attempt to join the faculty of a university, he settled for a menial job in the Patent Office at Bern. While he was a clerk, he checked thousands of patents in working hours and, on his own time, wrote ten scientific papers that astounded scholars. For several years, Einstein kept the lowly position that gave him plenty of free time to study and to think. In the years at Bern, he actually laid the foundation for his later contributions to science, which were to revolutionize modern physics and set us in the path toward the space age.

The back of Einstein's desk drawers was filled with small bits of paper on which he had scribbled notes on his theories of physics and on other scientific matters. Years later those scraps of paper were assembled and from them he published his revolutionary theory of relativity. The refinement and extension of his early theories brought him great popular acclaim, greater probably than that of any other scientist in world history.

By the time Einstein was appointed assistant professor at the Zurich Polytechnic Institute, he was considered by his colleagues to be definitely odd, a character. He made a bad impression as a professor and as a person. He dressed unconventionally in baggy clothes and sloppy tennis shoes, and his long hair was unkempt. Worse yet, by conventional, academic practice, he had no clear-cut curriculum for his students and simply talked with them about his ideas. However, in spite of his untidy appearance and his vague methods of instruction, the fame of Einstein was growing.

He was offered a full professorship at the German University at Prague and went there in 1911. He refused to be drawn into petty political intrigues that were carried on by faculty members, and in 1913, he thankfully returned to Zurich as full professor. A year later, friends prevailed on him to take a full professorship at the University of Berlin, and he did accept the offer on condition that he be allowed to retain his Swiss citizenship.

Those who knew Einstein well at that time have stated that the place were he lived and the academic status he achieved really mattered very little to him. He wanted only to be free to think in quiet and solitude wherever he was.

When World War I broke out in August 1914, Einstein was at first bewildered by the frenzy of his colleagues, and was then angered by their attitude. He himself refused to be drawn into the conflict and for his aloof dismissal of the problems of war, he was ostracized by his fellow-scientists. He ignored his peers as well as the war and, after making clear his own pacifist views, continued his own work. Germany after the first world war was a defeated country in which hatred boiled. Some of the hate was turned toward Einstein whose new theories had upset the very foundations of contemporary physics. People were all too willing to pounce on Einstein, the ac-

knowledged pacifist, and to accuse him of partial re-
sponsibility for Germany's misfortunes. Both he and
his theories were bitterly attacked and loudly de-
nounced by Germans. French scientists, quick to hate
all Germans at that point in history, shouted their
denunciation of Einstein and what they called his
heretical theories.

Anti-Semitism was growing and Einstein, who
took his Jewish religion seriously, was a main target
for the anti-Semites, particularly in Germany. He
was forced at last to give up his detached attitude and
to take a stand in open defense of Jews. He was
caught between a passionate desire for social justice
and an abhorrence of involvement in contemporary
issues. Gradually and inevitably he was drawn into
international events that centered on the problem of
minority groups.

Although he had to take a stand on certain issues
of the time, he continued what for him was a normal
life. He took part in musicales at home, and spent
hours reading. He was a big man, rippling with
powerful muscles which he exercised and developed
with his favorite sport, sailing. He spent hours sailing
his boat while he thought through problems of physics and mathematics and philosophy.

Einstein was a theoretical physicist. Unlike our
picture of a scientist carrying on investigations with

elaborate apparatus in his laboratories, Einstein used his amazing mind to think through problems in a theoretical manner. Like Newton, he asked the right questions and by applying his vast knowledge to the questions he mathematically deduced what should be the right answers. For nearly fifty years thousands of scientists have taken his deductions, experimented with them in a physical manner. Continuously they have found that he was correct and did lead science toward totally new interpretations.

His first great contribution was a new conception of the theory of Brownian movement; then he added significantly to a new and different understanding of the photoelectric effect. In 1905 he published his own theory of *special relativity* on the electrodynamics of moving bodies and on the equivalence of mass and mechanical energy. His theory was hailed by some, scorned by others. But Einstein's special relativity contained the facts which gave a new and accelerated direction to research on the atom.

In 1911 he proposed the astounding idea of the equivalence of mass and inertia. By 1916 he had completed his mathematical formulation of a *general theory of relativity* which included gravitation as a determining factor of the curvature of a space-time continuum and stated that *gravitation was a field rather than a force.* He was awarded the Nobel Prize in 1921 for his proven theory of the photoelectric effect.

Around him swirled a tornado of publicity. Newspaper headlines announced his theories which were as difficult to simplify then as they are now. The general public read such incorrect stories as those which stated that "only four men are capable of understanding the revolutionary ideas of Albert Einstein." Throughout the world newspaper readers gasped and gaped in awe. Hundreds of capable scientists studied his theories and began applying them to their own research projects which shifted the direction of physics, chemistry, astronomy and many other fields of scientific investigation.

He progressed with his work and was much in demand as a lecturer who spoke bluntly, without diplomacy. He fulfilled speaking engagements in Europe, England, and in the United States. In 1932 Einstein lectured at the California Institute of Technology and, while he was still in the United States, was offered a permanent post at the Institute for Advanced Study in Princeton, New Jersey. That Institute was planned by Dr. Abraham Flexner as a center where men of the highest intellectual quality could be free to carry on their investigations, without the demands of teaching.

Einstein refused the invitation. He sailed for Germany where Hitler had come to full power, and persecution of the Jews was well-launched. Einstein had childlike faith that even though he was a Jew, he could live safely in the country where he had been born. When he arrived in Germany he was forced to face facts: Jews were being persecuted and he was a principal target. Reluctantly and sadly, he packed his few belongings and sailed back to the United States, to the Institute. There he found what he had sought throughout his life—the perfect place for undisturbed thought. There, too, he finally realized that one cannot be a pacifist in a world where there are aggressors who seem dedicated to slaughter.

With a second world war threatening every country, scientists wanted the idea of creating an atom bomb to be directly presented to the President of the United States. Men of science were convinced that the bomb could be built, and the men they chose to represent them and their idea were Albert Einstein, Niels Bohr and a few other internationally famous scientists.

The pacifist on whom the world had forced the admission that under certain circumstances one must fight, agreed to write to the President of the United States. After anguished hours of thought, Einstein made his decision and composed the letter. Franklin D. Roosevelt then ordered research to begin on creating a bomb which he did not live to see burst.

Einstein did live to know that the bomb was dropped. He also lived long enough to know that his daringly imaginative scientific thinking had completely revolutionized modern physics, had opened the door to untold benefits from peacetime uses of atomic energy.

Although he was able to continue his contemplation of theoretical physics his seclusion in Princeton was no longer real seclusion. He was swept into a scientific, social and political series of events pertaining to injustice and human welfare until the day he died on April 18, 1955—one of the most recent in a long list of scientists whose ideas changed the world in which we live.

INDEX

INDEX

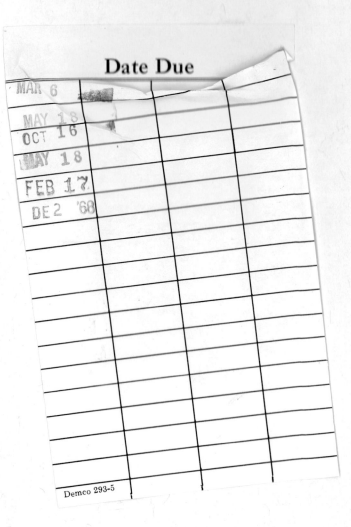

Date Due

MAR 6			
MAY 18			
OCT 16			
MAY 18			
FEB 17			
DE 2 '68			

Demco 293-5